THE
KINGDOM
BOOKS

D1308629

THE
AMAZING
COLLECTION™

THE KINGDOM BOOKS

JOSHUA, JUDGES, RUTH, 1 SAMUEL,

2 SAMUEL, 1 KINGS, AND 2 KINGS

SET 2

BIG
DREAM
MINISTRIES

© 2004 by Big Dream Ministries, Inc.

No part of *The Amazing Collection*, whether audio, video, or print, may be reproduced in any form without written permission from Big Dream Ministries, Inc., P.O. Box 324, 12460 Crabapple Road, Suite 202, Alpharetta, Georgia 30004.
1-678-366-3460
www.theamazingcollection.org

ISBN-13: 978-1-932199-02-4
ISBN-10: 1-932199-02-0

Cover design by Brand Navigation and Arvid Wallen
Cover composite image by Getty Images and Corbis
Creative Team: Leigh McLeroy, Kathy Mosier, Pat Reinheimer, Glynese Northam

Printed in Canada

3 4 5 6 7 8 9 10 / 10 09 08

Welcome to
The Amazing Collection
The Bible, Book by Book

It is amazing how a love letter arriving at just the right time can gladden the heart, refresh the soul, and restore the passion of the beloved. When lovers are separated by distance and can communicate only through the written word, that word becomes the lifeline of their love.

The greatest love letter ever written often sits on our shelves unopened as we go about our lives, sometimes fearful, burdened, anxious, in pain, and in doubt, not knowing that on its pages we can find all we need to live the life we have always wanted.

In this love letter we will discover God, and through Him we will receive hope, assurance, freedom from fear, guidance for everyday life, wisdom, joy, peace, power, and above all, the way to salvation. We will find the life we have always longed for—*abundant* life.

The Bible is simply a love letter compiled into sixty-six books and written over a period of sixteen hundred years by more than forty authors living on three continents. Although the authors came from different backgrounds, there is one message, one theme, one thread that runs throughout the entire Bible from the first book, Genesis, to the last book, Revelation. That message is God's redeeming love for mankind—a message that is as relevant for us today as it was two thousand years ago.

God has written the Bible so that men and women might enter into an intimate relationship with Him and see His character, His works, His power, and His love. It would be tragic to read these books and never come to know your God! Therefore, as you go through this study, listen to the lectures, read the Scripture, and do your daily homework. Make it your heart's desire to know God intimately. Read each page of the Bible as if it were a love letter written by the hand of God to you personally. Bask in His great love, stand in awe of His mighty power, bow before His majesty, and give thanksgiving and adoration to the One who is all-present, all-knowing, all-merciful, and all-loving. He is on every page, and He is speaking to you.

The Bible is a book inspired by God Himself. It is His story, His love letter, His invitation to you to become His child through His Son, Jesus Christ. It is the Word of God . . . indeed, the most Amazing Collection.

CONTENTS

MAPS, CHARTS, AND DIAGRAMS

WORKBOOK GUIDE

The Amazing Collection is a study of the Bible, book by book. This second study focuses on the seven books of the Bible we have titled The Kingdom Books. The following will acquaint you with the design of this series.

One book of the Bible will be studied each week through a teaching video and a written study. The teaching video includes music to stir the heart, graphics to enlighten the mind, and a personal testimony to bring the theme of that particular book to life.

The workbook contains:

1. An introduction to summarize each book.

2. Outlines to be used while watching each of the teaching videos. The answers to the outline blanks are given during the videos and can also be found in the key at the back of your workbook.

3. *Learning for Life* discussion questions to be used after viewing the videos. (If your group is large, we recommend forming small discussion groups.)

4. Five daily lessons of homework for each book.

5. A memory verse for each book.

6. Various maps, charts, and diagrams.

7. A review at the end of each week to refresh your memory. The answers to the review are found in the *Review It!* sections in the margins at the end of the lessons for Day One through Day Four. The fifth review question is a review of the memory verse.

Before you begin the homework, ask God to show you how to apply the truths of Scripture to your own life. At the beginning of each day's lesson in the workbook, there are two choices for the daily reading. The *Complete Read* enables you to read one entire book of the Bible each week. During busy times, the *Quick Read* allows you to read a few key chapters or verses from that book. The daily lesson will require a small amount of time each day to complete. Of course, feel free to extend that time with additional study.

One of the incredible things about the Word of God is that you can read the same Scripture at different times in your life and gain new insights with each reading. God's Word is inexhaustible, and it is living; it has the power to produce life-changing results.

Our prayer for you as you begin your journey through *The Amazing Collection* is that you will learn for life the purpose, main characters, geography, and time period of every book in the Bible. But above all, we pray that you will come to know more intimately the God of the Bible, His Son Jesus Christ, and the Holy Spirit.

THE KINGDOM BOOKS AT A GLANCE

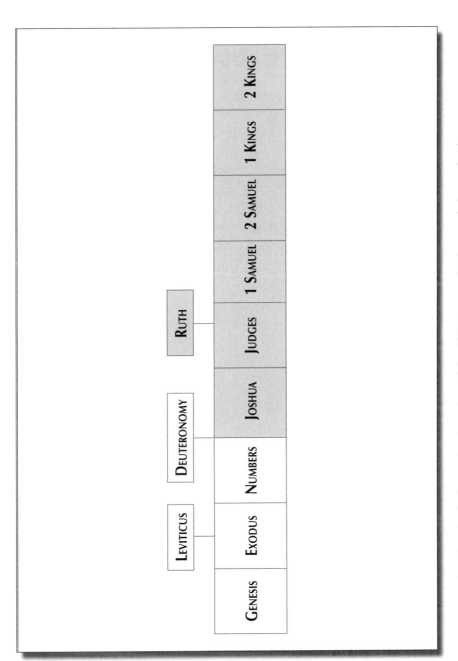

To see how these books fit into the chronology of the Old Testament books as a whole, see the chart on page 199.

OVERVIEW OF THE KINGDOM BOOKS

The following pages provide an overview of each of the books you will be studying in this set. They are designed to be cut out and used as quick reference cards with the main facts of the book on the front and the memory verse on the back.

You might find it helpful to laminate them and carry them with you on a ring or keep them in a card holder in a place where you'll be able to refer to them often.

It is our hope that this will be a tool that will help you truly learn these books for life.

JOSHUA
Land Conquered

WHO: | **WHAT:** | **WHERE:**
Joshua | Land Conquered | Canaan
 | Land Divided |

Time Covered: 25 Years

JUDGES
Judges Ruled

WHO: | **WHAT:** | **WHERE:**
Deborah | 7 Sin Cycles | Israel
Gideon | |
Samson | |

Time Covered: 340 Years

RUTH
Redemption Defined

WHO: | **WHAT:** | **WHERE:**
Naomi | Love Story | Moab
Ruth | | Bethlehem
Boaz | |

Time Covered: About 30 Years

JOSHUA
Land Conquered

So the LORD gave Israel all the land which He had sworn to give to their fathers, and they possessed it and lived in it.

JOSHUA 21:43

JUDGES
Judges Ruled

In those days there was no king in Israel; everyone did what was right in his own eyes.

JUDGES 21:25

RUTH
Redemption Defined

Blessed is the LORD who has not left you without a redeemer today.

RUTH 4:14

1 SAMUEL
Monarchy Established

WHO:
Samuel
Saul
David

WHAT:
Last Judge (Samuel)
First King (Saul)

WHERE:
Canaan

Time Covered: 94 Years

2 SAMUEL
David's Throne Established

WHO:
David

WHAT:
Davidic Covenant

WHERE:
Judah
Israel

Time Covered: 40 Years

1 KINGS
Kingdom Divided

WHO:
Solomon
Rehoboam
Elijah
Jezebel

WHAT:
Temple Built
Nation Divided

WHERE:
Israel
Judah

Time Covered: 120 Years

1 SAMUEL
Monarchy Established

Man looks at the outward appearance,
but the Lord *looks at the heart.*

1 Samuel 16:7

2 SAMUEL
David's Throne Established

May the house of Your servant David
be established before You.

2 Samuel 7:26

1 KINGS
Kingdom Divided

For when Solomon was old,
his wives turned his heart away after other gods.

1 Kings 11:4

2 KINGS
Kingdoms Exiled

WHO:	**WHAT:**	**WHERE:**
Elijah	Kingdoms Exiled	Israel to Assyria
Elisha		Judah to Babylonia
Kings of Israel		
Kings of Judah		

Time Covered: 293 Years

2 KINGS
Kingdoms Exiled

They rejected His statutes and His covenant which He made with their fathers and His warnings with which He warned them.

2 KINGS 17:15

Introduction to THE KINGDOM BOOKS

The books of Genesis through Esther are usually referred to as the Historical Books because they tell the story in historical and sequential form. We have divided these seventeen books into three sets: The Pentateuch, The Kingdom Books, and The Post-Exilic Books.

Throughout The Pentateuch, we met God Almighty and found Him to be the Creator (Genesis), the Deliverer (Exodus), the Law Giver (Leviticus), the One who disciplines (Numbers), and the One who gives blessings for obedience and curses for disobedience (Deuteronomy). God also proved to be a Promise Giver. In Genesis, God promised He would give Abraham land and a great number of descendants. Those descendants would become the nation that would be a blessing to all the nations on earth. It was quite a promise — but then He is quite a God.

In The Kingdom Books, we will see that God is a Promise Keeper. He had indeed given His people the land He had promised them, but the land was under the control of the Canaanites. The land was rich and fertile, but the inhabitants were fierce, experienced warriors. It would have been an impossible mission had not the God of the universe, the all-powerful One, been on their side.

Those entering the Promised Land were the children of those who had left Egypt; therefore, many of them had only heard of God's faithfulness as He led their parents through the wilderness to the Promised Land. Yet through Moses' capable leadership, they were strong in their faith and determined to obey the living God and establish a land and a nation that would be a blessing to all the earth. So with their confidence in Yahweh, the Israelites began the march into the land God had given them.

The Kingdom Books, Joshua through 2 Kings, include the conquering of the land, the ruling of the judges, and the uniting and the dividing of the kingdom. These books end with Israel conquered and scattered and Judah destroyed and exiled.

Throughout the pages of The Kingdom Books you will come face-to-face with men and women of great courage resulting from great faith. They were not disappointed as God broke down walls, won battles, raised up kings and brought down nations, healed the sick and reversed death, sent chariots of fire, and purified poisonous waters. He blessed Israel when she obeyed and disciplined her when she rebelled. He sent prophets to warn and rulers to lead. He showed His glory in a temple built for His presence and His mercy as He dealt with the weak and faltering. He is God, and His character inhabits every page.

In these books, you will also get a glimpse of men and women as they walked and sometimes struggled with God. Don't miss the courage and devotion of men such as Joshua, Caleb, Gideon, Samuel, David, and Hezekiah. And pay special attention to those gallant women who made a great difference in their world: Rahab, Deborah, Ruth, Hannah, and Abigail. Great lessons can also be learned from those whose lives were not so sterling, such as Samson, Saul, and Jezebel.

Open these books and you will see the daily news, for some things never change. There are still evil rulers and suffering people. There are still civil wars and unjust leaders. There are still nations who experience God's great blessings and those who experience His discipline. Though nations rise up and are brought down, one thing remains the same: God is the ruler of all and it is in His hands and under His control. To God be the glory, great things He has done!

JOSHUA

ONE

[Land Conquered]

So the Lord gave Israel all the land which He had

sworn to give to their fathers, and they

possessed it and lived in it.

JOSHUA 21:43

JOSHUA
[Land Conquered]

INTRODUCTION

As the Israelites looked across the Jordan into the land God had promised to give them, they were well aware that the land was inhabited by giants. They had been wandering in the wilderness for forty years listening to stories of giants and of a God who is greater than any enemy. They had lived in discipline, waiting for the time when the wandering would be over and they would at last have a land of their own. Now the time had come. Moses, the only leader they had ever known, was dead. Joshua had taken his place and would not only lead them into battle but would also lead them in their spiritual walk with God.

Joshua followed God, and the people followed Joshua. Once again, a body of water was parted by God, and once again, the children of Israel walked safely across. As they prepared for their first battle, they received instructions from Joshua that could be obeyed only if they had absolute faith in the power of God to help them. They were not disappointed. As they circled Jericho one last time, the walls came down and the battle was won, not because of their great prowess as warriors, but because of the power of God to fight on their behalf.

This book covers twenty-five years. It took the Israelites just over seven years to conquer the inhabitants of Canaan and take the land. Then the land was divided among the tribes. The book ends with the death of Joshua.

JOSHUA
[Land Conquered]

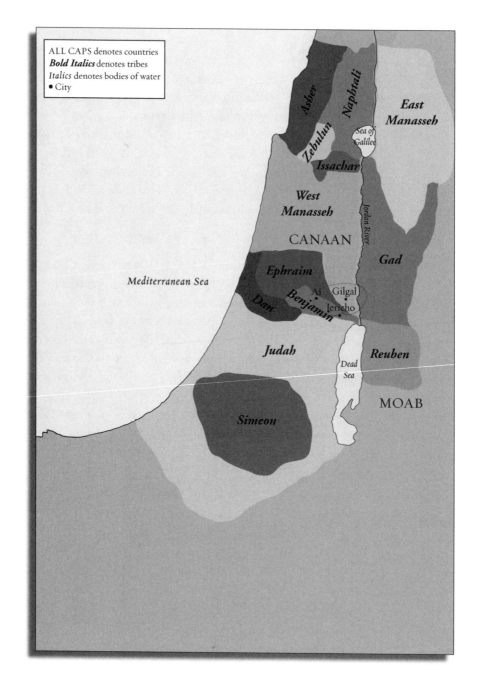

ALL CAPS denotes countries
Bold Italics denotes tribes
Italics denotes bodies of water
● City

Asher

Naphtali

East Manasseh

Zebulun

Sea of Galilee

Issachar

West Manasseh

CANAAN

Jordan River

Gad

Ephraim

Mediterranean Sea

Ai
● Gilgal
Dan
Benjamin
Jericho ●

Judah

Reuben

Dead Sea

MOAB

Simeon

JOSHUA
[Land Conquered]

OVERVIEW

WHO: Author: Joshua
               Main Character: Joshua

WHAT: Conquering and settling the Promised Land

WHEN: The book covers 25 years (1405–1380 BC)

WHERE: Almost the entire book takes place in Canaan

WHY: The Israelites, led by Joshua, conquered and settled the land God promised them

I.   THE ISRAELITES _____ THE PROMISED LAND (JOSHUA 1–5).

     A. God gave a _____ to Joshua (Joshua 1).

     B. Joshua sent out two _____ (Joshua 2).

     C. God parted the _____ River and the Israelites crossed over (Joshua 3–4).

     D. Joshua _____ the captain of the Lord's host (Joshua 5).

II.   THE ISRAELITES _____ THE PROMISED LAND (JOSHUA 6–12).

     A. God gave the Israelites victory at _____ (Joshua 6).

     B. Because of disobedience, the Israelites were disciplined at _____ (Joshua 7).

     C. The Israelites approach to Canaan was _____ and conquer (Joshua 9–12).

III. The Israelites _____ the land among
the twelve tribes (Joshua 13–24).

A. The _____ were allowed to live among the Israelites.

B. The _____ received the sacrifice of God as their
inheritance, not land (Joshua 21).

C. Joshua gave a final _____ to the people of Israel
(Joshua 22:24-28).

D. There were three burials at the end of Joshua (Joshua 24:29-33):

1. _____

2. _____

3. _____

Application

God's power easily defeats His children's foes. He is our defender, strength,
comfort, hope, and security. In Him we take our courage.

JOSHUA
[Land Conquered]

LEARNING FOR LIFE

1. Beginning in Genesis, build the foundation for the book of Joshua (group effort).

2. God gave Joshua specific instructions concerning the conquest of Jericho. Why did God choose this method, and why was this conquest so important to the Israelites?

3. What important lesson was learned at Ai? What can we learn from God's response to Achan's disobedience?

4. What does Joshua teach us about courage? In what areas of your life do you need courage?

JOSHUA
[Land Conquered]

DID YOU REALIZE?
Joshua was born as a
slave in Egypt.

DAY ONE

COMPLETE READ: Chapters 1–5
QUICK READ: Chapters 3–4

THE BIG PICTURE

We've worked our way through the Bible beginning with
Genesis, and now we have come to Joshua. And, finally, the children of Israel have come to their Promised Land.

The book of Joshua records the conquest and settlement of
the Promised Land of Canaan, initially promised to Abraham
in Genesis 12 and 13 around 2100 BC. Chapter 1 of Joshua
describes events taking place approximately 1400 BC. Seven
hundred years have elapsed since God first promised this land!
Seven centuries — three times longer than America has been
a nation. God seldom acts in a hurry! Between Abraham and
Joshua, generations have come and gone — all of them learning
about the land, hoping for the land, dreaming about the land,
and dying without the land. But now it is time for the promise to
be fulfilled, and Joshua is God's chosen leader. Moses had been
God's man to lead His people out of Egypt; Joshua is His man
to lead them into Canaan.

The book is named after its central figure, Joshua, which means
"Jehovah is salvation." Although difficult to prove, many scholars
believe that Joshua is the author of the book. Since the conquest
of the land occurred around 1400 BC and Joshua died about
1390 BC, he would have written the book sometime during that
ten-year period.

*I find His promises
unfolding like leaves in
spring, and there at the
center the kernel which
is His everlasting love —
His promise fulfilled in
me and for me.*
—MARGARET CUNDIFF,
spiritual writer

The chart that follows presents a broad overview of the content of the book:

CONQUEST		SETTLEMENT	
Entering the Land	Conquering the Land	Partitioning the Land	Living in the Land
1 5	6 12	13 21	22 24

During the seven-hundred-year interval between the promise of the land and its fulfillment, God's people lived first in Canaan and then in Egypt, most of that time in the bondage of slavery. God built the nation of Israel in Canaan through Abraham, Isaac, and Jacob. In Egypt, He built it through Jacob's descendants. But these years also revealed something about the Canaanites who lived in the land that Israel would eventually permanently possess.

Read Genesis 15:12-16 and state in your own words what God meant in the second half of verse 16 (reminder: Amorite is another name for Canaanite).

Now read Leviticus 18:24-28, which describes the condition of the Canaanites just prior to the Israelites' conquest of them. Compare these verses to what God had said about the Amorites (Canaanites) to Abraham in Genesis 15. What had happened in the intervening centuries?

INTERESTING!
Forty years of manna ceased just before the conquest of Jericho.

Have faith in God. Faith is really believing that something good will come to pass in spite of things that are looking clean contrary.

—FLORENCE ALLSHORN, missionary to Uganda

As you read and study the book of Joshua, you will see faith in God as a predominant motif. Consider making a log of the pictures of faith you find as you proceed through the book. You may want to use this simple outline:

WHO DISPLAYED FAITH	HOW THEY DISPLAYED FAITH	RESULT OF THEIR FAITH

MEMORY VERSE

So the LORD gave Israel all the land which He had sworn to give to their fathers, and they possessed it and lived in it.

JOSHUA 21:43

REVIEW IT!
The theme of Joshua is conquering and settling the Promised Land.

JOSHUA
[Land Conquered]

DAY TWO

COMPLETE READ: Chapters 6–10
QUICK READ: Chapter 1

THINK ABOUT IT
Joshua was to conquer
what God had already
given him.

A CRUCIAL CHAPTER

On November 22, 1963, an assassin's bullet killed John F. Kennedy, president of the United States. Those who were old enough on that day to understand the significance of the event will never forget where they were or how they felt when they heard the news. A country or group of people is most vulnerable during those minutes or hours or days in which they are leaderless. Within two hours, Vice President Lyndon B. Johnson stood aboard Air Force One, his wife on one side of him, the widow of the slain president on the other. He raised his hand and took the oath of office to become president of the United States. Obviously, this was his hour of greatest testing. And it was only natural that the pressure, the fear, and the wondering clearly marked his countenance.

In March 1405 BC, another great leader — possibly the greatest leader of all time — died. At a critical juncture in the life of the nation he had led, a new leader stood ready to step up to the task.

The leader who died was Moses. The new leader was Joshua. And the critical juncture was the eve of Israel's advance to conquer and settle the Promised Land.

Chapter 1 of Joshua is a Crucial Chapter because it describes what took place during that initial time of momentous transition: "Now it came about after the death of Moses the servant of the LORD, that the LORD spoke to Joshua the son of Nun, Moses' servant, saying . . ." (verse 1). What God told Joshua during this

To command is to serve, nothing more and nothing less.
—ANDRÉ MALRAUX,
twentieth-century French
novelist, adventurer, and
art historian

time of personal loss, grief, uncertainty, and fear was critical to his ability to function as he stepped into the sandals of his predecessor.

As you read Joshua 1:1-9, write down your thoughts to these questions:

What did God tell Joshua to do?

What promises did God make to Joshua?

Based on what God said, what human weaknesses in Joshua do you think He was aware of?

Give me the courage to take the road I should today, whatever it may mean, wherever it may lead. May I travel trustfully and obediently through this day, and tonight rest in Your peace.

—MARGARET CUNDIFF, spiritual writer

In verses 2-9, God mentioned Moses four times. Why do you think He did that?

Summarize your study by stating two or three major principles or truths that could be helpful in stepping into any difficult situation.

What in this chapter personally impacted you the most?

Memory Verse

So the LORD gave Israel all the land which He had sworn to give to their fathers, and they possessed it and lived in it.

JOSHUA 21:43

REVIEW IT!
Our Crucial Chapter is chapter 1 because it portrays Joshua's transition into Moses' leadership position.

JOSHUA
[Land Conquered]

FACT
Joshua conquered central Canaan first, next the south, and finally the north. This military strategy is called "divide and conquer."

DAY THREE

COMPLETE READ: Chapters 11–15
QUICK READ: Chapters 6–7

A PROMINENT PLAYER

In his book *The Life God Blesses*, Gordon MacDonald writes,

> Harry Emerson Fosdick, well-known preacher of an earlier era, frequently alluded to the Great Wall of China, erected by mass labor and heavy governmental expense. This wall seemed at the time to be the guarantee the Chinese were seeking that they would be safe from all invaders. But it didn't work. Not because it was inadequate as a physical barrier. But because guards along the wall were open to bribes. On one occasion Fosdick said, "It was the human element that failed. What collapsed was character which proved insufficient to make the great structure men had fashioned really work."[1]

The measure of a man's real character is what he would do if he knew he would never be found out.

—THOMAS BABINGTON MACAULAY, author and statesman

And without character on the part of Joshua, the great plan God had fashioned for conquering and settling the land of Canaan would also have been in jeopardy. Because of who Joshua had become under the tutelage of God and Moses, he was able to lead and persevere through the most trying circumstances. He is certainly a Prominent Player in this story.

Joshua's character had been forged while he was Moses' servant during the forty years of wandering. Read the following affirmations of Joshua's character and describe in your own words what each one means.

Numbers 27:18

Numbers 32:12

Deuteronomy 34:9

Joshua 6 and 7, the Quick Read for today, describe two
military encounters with very dissimilar circumstances, challenges, outcomes, and consequences. They both required a
leader of strong character, resolve, and trust to lead the people
to a successful conclusion. Read each story and summarize the
character traits in Joshua that were tested in each encounter.

Joshua 6:1-21

*We are the wire, God
is the current. Our
only power is to let
the current pass
through us.*

—CARLO CARRETTO,
twentieth-century
Catholic spiritual writer

Joshua 7:1-26

Novelist Henry James writes in *The Art of Fiction*, "What is character but the determination of incident? What is incident but the illustration of character?"[2]

This was true in Joshua's life. And it is true in your life as well. Describe a time when your godly character determined an incident and in turn was illustrated by the incident. Then thank God for the character traits He has built into you.

REVIEW IT!
A Prominent Player in the book is Joshua, who displays a strong, godly character.

MEMORY VERSE

So the LORD gave Israel all the land which He had sworn to give to their fathers, and they possessed it and lived in it.

JOSHUA 21:43

JOSHUA
[Land Conquered]

DAY FOUR

COMPLETE READ: Chapters 16–20
QUICK READ: Chapter 14

A NOTABLE FEATURE

Age is an issue of mind over matter. If you don't mind, it doesn't matter.

—MARK TWAIN

As soon as you feel too old to do a thing, do it.

—MARGARET DELAND

Do not deprive me of my age. I have earned it.

—MAY SARTON

It is not how old you are, but how you are old.

—MARIE DRESSLER

The great thing about getting older is that you don't lose all the other ages you've been.

—MADELEINE L'ENGLE

I married an archeologist because the older I grow, the more he appreciates me.

—AGATHA CHRISTIE, English mystery author

People are living longer than ever and therefore have more potential for continued contribution than their forebears had. The good news? This potential can produce a phenomenal impact for good in the world generally and in the church specifically. The bad news? We don't have many models showing us how to do this well. Enter our Notable Feature in the book of Joshua. His name is Caleb, and his story is recorded in chapter 14, the Quick Read for today.

We are first introduced to Caleb in the book of Numbers. He was forty when he was sent by Moses as one of the twelve spies to check out the Promised Land. Read Numbers 13:25–14:10 and 14:22-24 and write down what you learn about Caleb from this critical incident.

ANOTHER GREAT
VERSE!
The righteous man will
flourish like the palm
tree. . . . They will still
yield fruit in old age;
they shall be full of
sap and very green.
(Psalm 92:12,14)

Now read Joshua 14:6-15 and respond to the following questions and statements.

How did Caleb describe the twelve spies incident as he looked back on it from the perspective of an eighty-five-year-old man?

Use different words and phrases to picture how Caleb viewed himself at age eighty-five. If you want to see the follow-up to this passage, read Joshua 15:13-19.

List as many commendable traits as possible that you see in Caleb as an elderly man.

The older the fiddle the sweeter the tune.
—English proverb

Think about the elderly people you know. Is there someone who displays a number of these traits? Who is that person, and what traits does he or she display?

If you are now elderly or on your way to being so (which covers all of us!), what have you learned for or about yourself from this study? What would be good to talk to God about right now?

MEMORY VERSE

So the LORD gave Israel all the land which He had sworn to give to their fathers, and they possessed it and lived in it.

JOSHUA 21:43

REVIEW IT!
A Notable Feature of Joshua is the contribution of the elderly Caleb.

JOSHUA
[Land Conquered]

INSIGHT
The book of Joshua
records very few
failures on the part of
Israel or its leaders.

DAY FIVE

COMPLETE READ: Chapters 21–24
QUICK READ: Chapter 24

A TIMELESS PRINCIPLE

In Athens, Greece, a student was sentenced to eight months imprisonment on charges of marrying two women within forty-eight hours. He appealed the sentence and was set free pending a new trial. The court heard that Petros Novaras, twenty-nine, married Vassiliki Chioti on January 24, 1971, in the central Greek town of Lamia. They left in his car for their honeymoon. When they had engine trouble, he sent his wife down to Athens on a bus. In the meantime, he went to a suburb in Athens and married a twenty-nine-year-old woman. He then continued his honeymoon with his second wife. During the hearing, Petros testified, "Both families were putting unbearable pressure on me. So I decided to take them both so as not to hurt anybody's feelings."[3]

God calls sin adultery of the heart. It is what you give your heart away to other than the heart of God.

—JOHN ELDREDGE, author of Wild at Heart

Novaras couldn't decide between the two possible wives — so he took both. Surely he had to know it would never work, but the temptation to not choose still won out. And his indecision got him in big trouble.

Joshua knew this same problem could exist for the people he was leading, not in choosing a wife, but in choosing a god! He told his followers, "If it is disagreeable in your sight to serve the LORD, choose for yourselves today whom you will serve: whether the gods which your fathers served which were beyond the River, or the gods of the Amorites in whose land you are living; but as for me and my house, we will serve the LORD" (Joshua 24:15).

There were many options for the people when it came to gods. Canaanites still lived in the land, and they were very "religious" people. Ornaments and places of their paganism were within easy reach, and the pressure was strong. Some of the people were trying to play it both ways — worshiping God and worshiping other gods. So in one of the classic biblical exhortations, Joshua, the spiritually seasoned, godly, 110-year-old man of God, called for a decision. Choose God or choose gods. The people couldn't have both.

Prior to putting the decision before the people, Joshua quoted God extensively in Joshua 24:2-13. Summarize in one sentence what God was saying to the people and then explain why you think God, through Joshua, addressed the people in this manner.

Following Joshua's challenge to the people in Joshua 24:15, a dialogue took place in verses 16-28. First the people spoke . . . then Joshua . . . and the people . . . then Joshua . . . and the people . . . then Joshua. Describe what was said during this dialogue and what the final outcome was.

When we cease to worship God, we do not worship nothing, we worship anything.
—G. K. CHESTERTON,
English critic, journalist, and mystery novelist

In what ways can you identify with Joshua in this dialogue?

In what ways can you identify with the people in this dialogue?

Their gods were idols — tangible, visible objects of veneration. Our idols can be much more subtle — intangible, invisible enticements to veneration. An idol can be described as something we demand at all costs or anything other than God that we use to make our lives successful. It may be status, acceptance, our good works, pleasure, or control. Ask God to show you any competition to Him in your life. Talk to Him about the choice you face and about what it means for you to choose for yourself today whom you will serve. Then explain what He reveals to you.

It is comparatively easy to wait upon God; but to wait upon Him only — to feel, so far as our strength, happiness, and usefulness are concerned, as if all creatures and second causes were annihilated and we were alone in the universe with God is, I suspect, a difficult and rare attainment.

—E. M. Bounds, American spiritual writer

MEMORY VERSE

So the LORD gave Israel all the land which He had sworn to give to their fathers, and they possessed it and lived in it.

JOSHUA 21:43

JOSHUA
[Land Conquered]

REVIEW

1. The theme of Joshua is conquering and settling the _____ Land.

2. Our Crucial Chapter is chapter 1 because it portrays Joshua's transition into _____ leadership position.

3. A Prominent Player in the book is _____ , who displays a strong, godly character.

4. A Notable Feature of Joshua is the contribution of the elderly _____ .

5. "So the LORD gave Israel all the _____ which He had sworn to give to their fathers, and they possessed it and lived in it."

JOSHUA 21:_____

JUDGES

[Judges Ruled]

Two

In those days there was no king in Israel;

everyone did what was right in his own eyes.

JUDGES 21:25

JUDGES
[Judges Ruled]

INTRODUCTION

The Israelites had been commanded by God to utterly destroy all the inhabitants of Canaan because of their great wickedness. Yet Israel left a few Canaanites alive in the land, and this disobedience led to their undoing.

After the death of Joshua and the elders, the new generation became enamored with the Canaanite ways and soon bowed down to other gods. We learn that "everyone did what was right in his own eyes," causing the moral and spiritual fiber of the land to begin to unravel. Time and time again, Israel found herself under the control of enemies. Time and time again, she cried out to God. And time and time again, God heard her cry and sent help in the form of judges. These judges led the people to victory, but the people's devotion to God didn't last long. Soon everyone would do what was right in his own eyes, and the cycle would repeat itself.

The book of Judges ends in one of the darkest periods in Israel's history and sets the stage for the period of the kings.

JUDGES
[Judges Ruled]

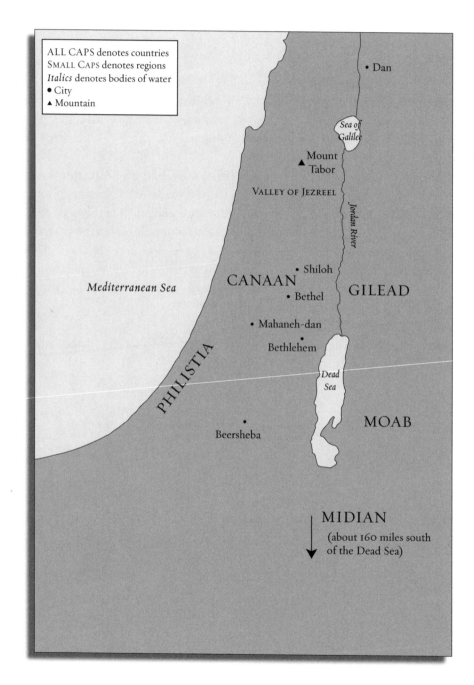

ALL CAPS denotes countries
SMALL CAPS denotes regions
Italics denotes bodies of water
• City
▲ Mountain

• Dan

Sea of Galilee

▲ Mount Tabor

VALLEY OF JEZREEL

Jordan River

• Shiloh

CANAAN

• Bethel

GILEAD

Mediterranean Sea

• Mahaneh-dan

Bethlehem •

Dead Sea

PHILISTIA

MOAB

•
Beersheba

MIDIAN
(about 160 miles south
of the Dead Sea)

UDGES
[Judges Ruled]

OVERVIEW

Who: Author: Anonymous (Talmud suggests Samuel)
Main Characters: Israel's judges: Deborah, Gideon, Samson

What: Everyone did as he pleased

When: 1390–1050 BC. Judges covers 340 years between the conquest of the land and Israel's monarchy

Where: Israel

Why: Shows the consequences of sin

I. THE _____ OF ISRAEL'S FAILURE (JUDGES 1–2)

A. Joshua died but his godly influence lived on through surviving

_____.

B. The Israelites rebelled against God and worshiped _____.

C. The elders died and the new generation did not know God nor the _____ He had done for Israel.

D. God's hand was against the Israelites, and they were oppressed and _____ by other nations.

E. The sin _____ followed this pattern: Israel rebelled — God rejected — Israel repented — God rescued — Israel rested.

F. There are _____ cycles of sin in the book of Judges.

II. THE _____ OF ISRAEL'S FAILURE (JUDGES 3–16)

A. Though a woman, _____ led Israel to victory against Jabor, king of Canaan.

1. Women are uniquely made to be uniquely used by God.

2. Under Deborah's rule, Israel enjoyed peace for _____ years.

B. Though a man with little courage, _____ led Israel to victory against the Midianites.

    1. God knows who we are, and He knows what we can become.

    2. God is not looking for my ability but for my availability.

    3. Under Gideon's rule, Israel enjoyed peace for _____ years.

C. Though weak in self-control, _____ destroyed the Philistine rulers.

    1. God is always ready to forgive when we ask Him.

    2. Samson led Israel for _____ years.

III. THE _____ OF ISRAEL'S FAILURE

    A. The Israelites did what was right in their _____ eyes.

    B. Wicked behavior shows the _____ of man without God.

APPLICATION

Godliness of the previous generation does not guarantee godliness of the present one.

JUDGES
[Judges Ruled]

LEARNING FOR LIFE

1. Beginning in Joshua, build the foundation for the book of Judges (group effort).

2. What are some of the characteristics of Deborah that help us see why God chose to use her in such a powerful way?

3. What was Samson's problem?

   a. How does the same problem manifest itself today?

   b. Samson's nation suffered as a result of his problem. In what ways does *our* nation suffer due to this problem?

4. Why did Gideon need a fleece from God? What does God's response tell you about Him?

5. Who will be the ultimate judge of all men? (See Revelation 19:11-16.)

JUDGES
[Judges Ruled]

DID YOU NOTICE?
In Joshua, Israel
conquered seven
nations. In Judges,
Israel was oppressed
by seven nations.

DAY ONE

COMPLETE READ: Chapters 1–2
QUICK READ: Chapters 1–2

THE BIG PICTURE

In the Bible, it takes only the turn of a page to get from the book of Joshua to the book of Judges. But that one turn opens the door to an entirely different world — a world that sharply contrasts the one we've just left behind.

A verse near the end of Joshua says, "Israel served the LORD all the days of Joshua and all the days of the elders who survived Joshua, and had known all the deeds of the LORD which He had done for Israel" (24:31).

By contrast, in the second chapter of the book of Judges we read, "All that generation also were gathered to their fathers; and there arose another generation after them who did not know the LORD, nor yet the work which He had done for Israel" (verse 10).

In your own words, briefly contrast the people described in these two verses.

Why does no one confess his sins? Because he is yet in them. It is for a man who has awoke from sleep to tell his dreams.
—SENECA, writer and philosopher (3 BC–AD 65)

Twice in the book of Judges, a telling statement is made: "Everyone did what was right in his own eyes" (17:6; 21:25).

Every person did just as he pleased. It is difficult to find anything positive in the book of Judges. As a result, we focus the contents of the book around the concept of failure:

DID YOU KNOW?
The first recorded parable in the Bible is found in Judges 9:7-15.

Causes of Failure	Cycles of Failure	Consequences of Failure
1:1 3:4	3:5 16:31	17:1 21:25

We will investigate the causes of failure on Day Two and the cycles of failure on Day Four. The third section, the consequences of failure, contains representative stories of idolatry and immorality that actually took place chronologically during the earlier part of the book. Placed where they are, they provide a graphic conclusion to the long-lasting cycles of sin and failure.

The book's events occurred during the centuries between the death of Joshua and the elders around 1390 BC and the death of Samson around 1050 BC — about 340 years.

It was common in ancient writings to title a book using the first word or phrase of the book. But because of the dominating role of the judges throughout the book, *Judges* was chosen as the title.

Though the Bible never states who wrote the book, evidence gained from details within the book itself points to Samuel. Jewish tradition also attributes authorship to him. The book of Judges was written approximately 1025 BC, twenty-five years after the death of Samson. Samuel, who we will meet again in the book of 1 Samuel, was a judge, a priest, and a prophet — a great leader in the history of Israel.

Here in the presence of Almighty God, I kneel in silence, and with penitent and obedient heart confess my sins, so that I may obtain forgiveness by Your infinite goodness and mercy. Amen.
—The Book of Common Prayer

This week as you read about so much failure, sadness, and tragedy, you might experience a broad range of emotions. As you become aware of those feelings, name and jot them down in the space that follows, along with the reference you were reading at the time. You might want to begin each day by asking God to give you holy humility and honesty as you read about the sins of others.

In Him the enslaved find redemption, the guilty pardon, the unholy renovation. In Him are everlasting strength for the weak, unsearchable riches for the needy, treasures of wisdom and knowledge for the ignorant, fullness for the empty. All this I have in Your Son Jesus; blessed be His name.

—Puritan prayer

REVIEW IT!
The theme of Judges is everyone did as he pleased.

MEMORY VERSE

In those days there was no king in Israel; everyone did what was right in his own eyes.

JUDGES 21:25

JUDGES
[Judges Ruled]

DAY TWO

COMPLETE READ: Chapters 3–8
QUICK READ: Chapters 3–4

A CRUCIAL CHAPTER

> On earth we are wayfarers, always on the go. This means
> that we have to keep moving forward. Therefore, be always
> unhappy about where you are if you want to reach where
> you are not. If you are pleased with what you are, you have
> stopped already. If you say, "It is enough," you are lost. Keep
> on walking, moving forward, trying for the goal.
> —SAINT AUGUSTINE OF HIPPO

If only the Israelites had believed and followed this truth. But
they did not. Joshua's job had been to conquer the land. Their job
was to occupy it. Joshua did his job. They failed to do theirs.

Prior to entering the land, God gave clear instructions for
what the people were to do once they entered the land. Read
Deuteronomy 7:1-5 and write down what God commanded
them to do and to avoid doing once they arrived.

WOW!
Samson is in the
unique company of
Isaac—both their births
were announced by the
angel of the Lord.

*What other dungeon is
so dark as one's own
heart! What jailer is as
inexorable as one's self!*
—NATHANIEL HAWTHORNE,
novelist and short story
writer (1804–1864)

Read the following passages and describe what the people actually did or failed to do. Relate these actions to the commands given by God that you identified in the previous question.

Judges 1:21-33

THINK ABOUT IT
The tragic end to
Abimelech's life
displays the principle of
reaping what we sow
found in Galatians 6:7.

Judges 2:11-13

Judges 3:5-7

*Can any sin be called
light, since every
sin involves some
contempt of God.*

—Eucherius, fifth-century
spiritual writer of
Western Orthodoxy

As you have seen, the basic failure of the Israelites is stated in the phrase, "they did not drive out" the inhabitants of the land. By allowing many of them to remain, they gave in to the temptation to intermarry with the people of the land and to embrace the worship of their gods. What God warned would happen if they did not obey did in fact happen. For centuries, these two problems remained in Israel and eventually became the reason God sent them into captivity. Thus our Crucial Chapter is chapter 1.

Regarding these events in the Old Testament, Paul wrote in 1 Corinthians 10:11, "Now these things happened to them as an example, and they were written for our instruction." What personal motivation are you gaining today from your study of this example?

The quick response to moral breakdown is to appoint committees to make new codes to guide our ethics. But we do not fail because we lack codes. We fail because we lack character.

—LEWIS B. SMEDES, author and professor at Fuller Theological Seminary

MEMORY VERSE

In those days there was no king in Israel; everyone did what was right in his own eyes.

JUDGES 21:25

REVIEW IT!
Our Crucial Chapter is chapter 1 because it describes the failure to drive out the inhabitants of the land.

JUDGES
[Judges Ruled]

DID YOU KNOW?
The period of the judges was almost as long as the period of Egyptian bondage.

DAY THREE

COMPLETE READ: Chapters 9–12
QUICK READ: Chapters 8:33–10:2

A NOTABLE FEATURE

This week we will reverse the normal order of A Prominent Player and A Notable Feature. This will make our study of the Prominent Players much richer.

The phrase "what goes around comes around" is familiar to all of us. When it relates to birthdays, holidays, and seasons, the cycle can bring enjoyment. When it relates to fashion and hairstyles, it can be amusing. But when "what goes around comes around" relates to drought or tornado season or the anniversary of an unhappy event, it can be very troubling. So it is with the seven cycles of sin found in the book of Judges. What went around came around.

Beginning in chapter 3 and continuing through chapter 16, the Notable Feature of Judges is described: seven cycles occur, all containing the same elements. The main players and the time frame in each cycle vary, but the progression is always the same:

1. The people fall into and pursue sin.

2. God disciplines them with the power of a foreign enemy.

3. The people cry out to God for relief.

4. God provides a judge who drives out the enemy.

5. A period of rest characterizes the people and the land until they fall into sin again and "what goes around comes around" — seven times.

Sin is a power in our life; let us fairly understand that it can only be met by another power.

—HENRY DRUMMOND, nineteenth-century scientist, evangelist, and author

Complete cycles one through three in the following chart by filling in the boxes with the appropriate Scripture passages from Judges. Include names and lengths of years when they are given. The fourth cycle is given as an illustration of what cycles one through three will look like when completed.

GEOGRAPHY TIME
Israel's enemies came from every direction on the compass.

The Cycles	1st Cycle 3:7-11	2nd Cycle 3:12-30	3rd Cycle 4:1–5:31	4th Cycle 6:1–8:32
People Rebelled				6:1
God Rejected				Midian 7 years 6:1
People Repented				6:6-7
God Sent Rescuer (Judge)				Gideon 6:11–8:28
Period of Rest				40 years 8:28

Even though you investigated only three of the seven cycles (the rest are more of the same and sometimes even worse), write down your thoughts to the following questions.

What thoughts or feelings did you have about the people?

God's coming is bound to His promise, not to our works or virtue. . . . God is thrust onward by His love, not attracted by our beauty. He comes even in moments when we have done everything wrong, when we have done nothing . . . when we have sinned.

—Carlo Carretto,
The God Who Comes

Whatever weakens reason; whatever impairs the tenderness of your conscience; whatever obscures your sense of God; whatever increases the authority of your body over your mind; whatever takes away your relish for spiritual things; that to you is sin, no matter how innocent it is in itself.

—Susanna Wesley, mother of John and Charles Wesley, English Methodist preachers

What thoughts or feeling did you have about God?

It is common to hear the God of the Old Testament described as a God of wrath in contrast to the God of the New Testament as a God of grace. On the basis of God's actions in the sections you studied today, how would you respond to that contrast?

Is there anything in your life that fits the "what goes around comes around" motif? If so, what would you like to say to God about that right now?

REVIEW IT!
The occurrence of seven cycles, each with the same events, is the Notable Feature of Judges.

Memory Verse

In those days there was no king in Israel; everyone did what was right in his own eyes.

JUDGES 21:25

JUDGES
[Judges Ruled]

DAY FOUR

COMPLETE READ: Chapters 13–16
QUICK READ: Chapter 16

NOTE
The rule of some of
the judges overlapped
because not all of them
ruled the entire land.

PROMINENT PLAYERS

When you hear the word *judge*, what words, feelings, or pictures come into your mind? Write them in the space below.

Most of us think of a person in a black robe invested with authority to preside over legal matters and to ensure that due legal procedure is properly administered. But our Prominent Players in the book of Judges were vastly different. Read Judges 2:11-19 and write down your thoughts to the following questions.

What were some of the responsibilities of the judges?

Most high and eternal
Strength, deliver me.
—Gallican Sacramentary

What was the relationship between the judges and God?

What was the relationship between the judges and the people?

The typical meaning of the word *judge* in the Hebrew language is "to make a decision between two or more alternative possibilities"[1]—much as we think of the word. But the word in this sense is used only once in the book of Judges. Leon Wood, in his book *The Distressing Days of the Judges*, describes the broader, more unique meaning as it applies to the judges in the book of Judges:

> The unique meaning does not exclude the more common one, but adds to it a basic and more inclusive concept. Put briefly, that concept is "service as leader." This leadership need not have excluded the work of deciding cases, especially when major problems were involved, but it centered in the disposal of administrative duties necessary to leadership.
>
> This leadership could be of a military nature as well as civil. In fact, this was clearly the case for at least six of the judges. Indeed, the activity of serving in the sense of *shaphat* is applied to the first judge, Othniel, only in conjunction with his work of military achievement; Judges 3:10 states, "And he judged [*shaphat*] Israel, and went out to war. . . ."
>
> More frequently, however, the word is used when the duties in mind were those of a civil nature. . . . The duties in view, when the word is so used, would have concerned a general supervision of the people, in whatever portion of the total land the judge served.[2]

The judges, understood in this way, functioned only during the period of the judges—about 340 years. The judges' leadership was then replaced by the rule of the kings. Interestingly, Samuel, the last judge, anointed Saul, the first king. Therefore, the role of the judge as leader in Israel, though short-lived by comparison, stands side by side with the roles of prophet, priest, and king — divinely ordained positions God used to give direction to His people.

Though the period of the judges is a dark period spiritually, there are bright spots in the lives of some of the individual judges. Read Judges 6:6-24 and write down your impressions of Gideon and his relationship with God.

The judges certainly carried a significant responsibility in giving oversight to God's people. In every generation, leadership like this is challenging and difficult. In your life, who fills this role for you? List the person(s) by name.

Take time right now to pray for their spiritual protection, courage, and wisdom as they faithfully try to serve God in that position.

MEMORY VERSE

In those days there was no king in Israel; everyone did what was right in his own eyes.

JUDGES 21:25

REVIEW IT!
The judges are the Prominent Players in the book of Judges, carrying a wide range of responsibilities.

JUDGES
[Judges Ruled]

CURRENT EVENTS
The first naval
expedition on record
occurred during the
time of the judges.

DAY FIVE

COMPLETE READ: Chapters 17–21
QUICK READ: Chapter 2

A TIMELESS PRINCIPLE

He's a chip off the old block! The apple never falls far from the tree.

Both of these statements describe a child's obvious similarity to a parent. The child may look, talk, walk, or act just like his or her mom or dad. And these traits are sometimes even carried into further generations. Many times a grandchild will look like or have the mannerisms of one of the grandparents — which, of course, is a highlight of a grandparent's life!

But there is one facet of life that is not passed down through the genes: Every generation must make its own decision about following God. The godliness of a previous generation does not guarantee the godliness of the present generation. God has no grandchildren.

The contrast between the people in Joshua and the people in Judges illustrates this Timeless Principle so clearly. Consider these differences:

Father, You are full of compassion. I commit and commend myself unto You, in whom I am, and live, and know. Be the Goal of my pilgrimage, and my Rest by the way.

—SAINT AUGUSTINE OF HIPPO, Carthaginian author and church father

JOSHUA	JUDGES
Obedience	Disobedience
Belief	Unbelief
Progress	Decline
Unity	Disunity
Joy	Sorrow
Faithfulness	Faithlessness
Victory	Defeat

Read Joshua 24:14-31 and then answer the following questions concerning this generation's spiritual attitudes and condition.

How serious do you think they were? Explain.

IMPORTANT
Baal worship,
introduced during this
period, remained a
serious problem for
God's people until the
Babylonian Captivity
eight hundred
years later.

What was their motivation for their spiritual fervor?

What did they seem to know about God that influenced them?

What words or phrases would you use to describe them?

Now read Judges 2:6-23 and describe this generation's spiritual attitudes and condition by answering the questions that follow.

What were some of their major spiritual weaknesses?

O eternal goodness, O eternal mercy! O hope and refuge of sinners! O immeasurable generosity! O eternal, infinite Good! O mad lover! Finite language cannot express the emotion of the soul who longs for You infinitely.

—CATHERINE OF SIENA, fourteenth-century Italian mystic, religious leader, and saint

What words would you use to contrast them with the previous generation?

Based on this passage, what would you say was the key difference between them and the previous generation that led them to reject God?

As parents, we can train our children in godliness, we can model a God-honoring lifestyle for them, we can pray for their spiritual well-being, we can send them to all the right places with all the right influences. We may influence our children, but we cannot control their spiritual journey. In the same way, each of us must respond to God's call on our lives individually. We cannot ride the coattails of our parents, and neither can our children ride ours.

How does this truth, so graphically portrayed in the book of Judges, impact you? What thoughts have you had? Is there anything you need to do? Is there something you need to take to God in prayer? Take time to respond in a way that is appropriate for you at this moment.

People frequently ask if I expected my children to become believers. I usually reply that the gospel is powerful and attractive. It uniquely meets the needs of fallen humanity. Therefore, I expected that God's Word would be the power of God to salvation for my children. But that expectation was based on the power of the gospel and its suitability to human need, not on a correct formula for producing children who believe.

—TEDD TRIPP,
Shepherding a Child's Heart

MEMORY VERSE

In those days there was no king in Israel; everyone did what was right in his own eyes.

JUDGES 21:25

JUDGES
[Judges Ruled]

REVIEW

1. The theme of Judges is everyone did as he _____.

2. Our Crucial Chapter is chapter 1 because it describes the failure to drive out the _____ of the land.

3. The occurrence of seven _____, each with the same events, is the Notable Feature of Judges.

4. The _____ are the Prominent Players in the book of Judges, carrying a wide range of responsibilities.

5. "In those days there was no _____ in Israel; everyone did what was right in his own eyes."

JUDGES 21:_____

RUTH

[Redemption Defined]

Blessed is the LORD *who has not left you*

without a redeemer today.

RUTH 4:14

RUTH
[Redemption Defined]

INTRODUCTION

In the dark period at the end of Judges, the book of Ruth emerges as a small ray of light. It is a beautiful love story, a picture of hope and loyalty, and a lovely look at a kinsman redeemer in the flesh.

The book of Ruth shines a light on two remarkable women in the midst of a nation that was coming undone spiritually. As we begin to read, we find Naomi and Ruth living in Moab. After the death of her husband and two sons, Naomi thought she had lost everything. She was an Israelite living in enemy territory. Ruth, Naomi's daughter-in-law, was a Gentile — a Moabite — at home in a godless society, a widow unfamiliar with the Living God except through Naomi's stories. Both women had little hope, yet they clung to the thin thread that perhaps God had not deserted them.

Naomi returned to Bethlehem in Judah, and Ruth, out of loyal love, followed her. The broken-hearted women found that the God they served had not forgotten them. In Boaz, He provided a kinsman redeemer to rescue them and give them love and joy, safety and security. This book is a beautiful romance, with each of the four chapters filled with lessons for today.

Ruth
[Redemption Defined]

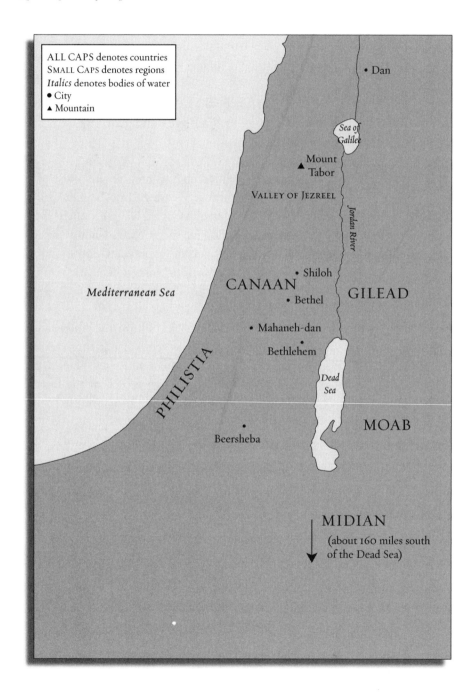

ALL CAPS denotes countries
SMALL CAPS denotes regions
Italics denotes bodies of water
• City
▲ Mountain

• Dan

Sea of Galilee

▲ Mount Tabor

VALLEY OF JEZREEL

Jordan River

• Shiloh

CANAAN

• Bethel

GILEAD

Mediterranean Sea

• Mahaneh-dan

• Bethlehem

Dead Sea

PHILISTIA

MOAB

• Beersheba

MIDIAN
(about 160 miles south of the Dead Sea)

RUTH

[Redemption Defined]

OVERVIEW

WHO: Author: Thought to be the prophet Samuel
Main Characters: Naomi, Ruth, Boaz

WHAT: Living out the law of the kinsman redeemer

WHEN: Sometime during the time of the judges (1390–1050 BC); covers about 30 years

WHERE: The book opens in the heathen land of Moab but ends in the birthplace of redemption: Bethlehem, Israel

WHY: God provides redemption for all mankind

I. THE HEATHEN: RUTH (RUTH 1)

A. The Historical Background of Ruth

1. Bethlehem means "House of _____"; yet at the time of Ruth, Bethlehem was experiencing a famine.

2. Elimelech means "My God is _____."

3. Mahlon means "_____," and Chilion means "pining."

4. Naomi means "_____" or "pleasant."

5. Because there was a famine, Elimelech took his family to Moab, a country that was Israel's _____.

B. The Helplessness of Ruth

1. Elimelech _____.

2. Mahlon and Chilion married _____ women.

3. Mahlon and Chilion _____.

C. Their only hope was for a _____.

1. Kinsman means "relative or kin."

2. Redeemer means "to buy back" or "to reclaim ownership."

3. The requirements of a kinsman redeemer were:

a. He must be _____.

b. He must be _____ to pay the price.

c. He must be _____ to reclaim ownership.

D. A Flicker of _____ for Ruth

1. Ruth _____ her heart and life to God and Naomi.

2. Ruth and Naomi returned to _____ .

3. Naomi renamed herself "Mara" or " _____ ."

II. The Hope: Boaz (Ruth 2–3)

A. Ruth began working in Boaz's field.

B. Boaz offered provision and protection for Ruth.

C. Boaz became Ruth's _____ .

1. He was _____ .

2. He was _____ .

3. He was _____ .

D. Boaz and Ruth married.

III. The Heir: Obed (Ruth 4)

A. Obed was Ruth's son, and his name means "servant."

B. Obed's son was _____ .

C. Jesse was the father of _____ , who became the king of Israel.

D. David was in the line of _____ , the King of kings and Lord of lords.

E. Jesus is our _____ .

1. He is _____ .

2. He was _____ to pay the price for our sins.

3. He is _____ .

Application

We all have a need of and hope for a Redeemer.

RUTH
[Redemption Defined]

LEARNING FOR LIFE

1. Beginning with the book of Joshua, trace the history of Israel from Joshua to the book of Ruth (group effort).

2. Boaz was Ruth's kinsman redeemer. Who is our Redeemer? (See Galatians 4:4-5.)

3. What are some of Ruth's characteristics that make her such an outstanding example for us today?

4. What was the progression of Ruth's relationship with her mother-in-law, Naomi?

5. What is one lesson from the book of Ruth that you can apply to your life today?

Ruth
[Redemption Defined]

GOOD COMPANY
Ruth is one of four
Gentile women listed
in the genealogy of
Jesus Christ.

DAY ONE

COMPLETE READ: Chapters 1–4

QUICK READ: Chapters 1–4

THE BIG PICTURE

Ruth is one of only two women in the Bible who have entire books devoted to them. The other woman is Esther, and the contrasts between their books are striking.

RUTH	ESTHER
A Gentile who married a Jew	A Jew who married a Gentile
Book begins with a famine	Book begins with a feast
Book ends with the birth of a baby	Book ends with the death of 75,000 people
She became an ancestress of the Messiah	She became a savior of the Messiah's people
God is mentioned 25 times	God is not mentioned once

If Christ lives in us, controlling our personalities, we will leave glorious marks on the lives we touch. Not because of our lovely characters, but because of His.

—EUGENIA PRICE, twentieth-century American southern writer

Though very different from each other, Ruth and Esther were strong women of faith, committed to carrying out the will of God regardless of the circumstances and the potential consequences.

Ruth 1:1 sets the time for the events of the book of Ruth: "Now it came about in the days when the judges governed. . . ." Into the dark days of the judges comes this lone bright spot of love and hope. Just as chapters 17–21 of Judges are illustrations of how bad things really were during that period, the book of Ruth is set as an illustration of one of the few good things that took place. We will look more closely at the concept of living well in the midst of bad times when we look at the Timeless Principle on Day Five.

It has been very difficult to determine authorship of the book, though many scholars believe Samuel is a reasonable speculation. The events of the book most likely occurred around 1140 BC, during the time that Gideon served as judge. Because of the reference to David in the last verse of the book, authorship is estimated at about 1000 BC, during the reign of David.

Because Ruth is the major character of the story, the chart that follows focuses on her activities within the story.

Ruth's Commitment to Naomi	Ruth's Introduction to Boaz	Ruth's Request of Boaz	Ruth's Marriage to Boaz
Chapter 1	Chapter 2	Chapter 3	Chapter 4

W. G. Scroggie writes, "Ruth is a lovely idyll, the tale of a friendship between two women, and the grand climax up to which all is working in the birth of a baby."[1] This quote indicates two purposes for the book. The first is a story of true loving friendship. The second is an insight into the genealogy of David (the baby mentioned by Scroggie), and therefore the genealogy of Jesus Christ.

Additionally, the faithful responsibility of Boaz to Ruth in living out the law of the kinsman redeemer points to the redeeming love of Jesus Christ for us. We will study this on Day Four as our Notable Feature. The importance of the kinsman redeemer in this book also provides our theme: living out the law of the kinsman redeemer.

As you read each day, try to get into the hearts of the characters. Try to imagine what they might have thought and felt.

God does not love us because we are valuable. We are valuable because God loves us.
—FULTON J. SHEEN, American Catholic clergyman and evangelist of the twentieth century

Based on your first reading today, what thoughts do you have about any of the characters?

REVIEW IT!
The theme of Ruth is living out the law of the kinsman redeemer.

MEMORY VERSE

Blessed is the LORD who has not left you without a redeemer today.

RUTH 4:14

RUTH
[Redemption Defined]

DAY TWO

COMPLETE READ: Chapters 1–4
QUICK READ: Chapter 1

INTERESTING!
In Judges, foreigners
chasten Israel. In Ruth,
a foreigner chooses
Israel.

A CRUCIAL CHAPTER

In 1860, the American writer Ralph Waldo Emerson wrote in his book *The Conduct of Life*, "The efforts which we make to escape from our destiny only serve to lead us into it."[2] No statement could be truer for Elimelech, the husband of Naomi and the father-in-law of Ruth. In chapter 1, we read that a famine had struck the land of Judah, and, trying to escape its hardships, Elimelech moved his family to the land of Moab. But there were a few problems: First, Moab was Israel's enemy and had invaded Israel a short time earlier. Second, Moab was disdained by God. And finally, Moab provided the temptation for Elimelech's sons to marry forbidden Gentile women.

Warren Wiersbe, in his commentary titled *Be Committed*, writes about Elimelech and his family and their thought that they could escape death by fleeing to Moab: "The family had planned only to 'sojourn' temporarily in Moab, but they remained for ten years (Ruth 1:4). At the end of that decade of disobedience, all that remained were three lonely widows and three Jewish graves in a heathen land. Everything else was gone."[3]

But God was still God. And He wove this tale of disaster into one of the most beautiful stories of the Bible, eventually giving us a compelling picture of redemption as Boaz fulfilled the law of the kinsman redeemer by marrying Ruth.

Providence is the almighty and ever present power of God by which He upholds, as with His hand, heaven and earth and all creatures, and so rules them that . . . all things come to us not by chance, but from His fatherly hand.

—The Heidelberg Catechism

In this Crucial Chapter, all the pieces are put in place. Read verses 1-18 and list all the events that had to take place for the story to climax in chapter 4 with the marriage of Boaz and Ruth.

Concentrate on verses 15-18. Take into account the stigma attached to a Moabitess moving to Judah as described in Deuteronomy 23:3: "No Ammonite or Moabite shall enter the assembly of the LORD; none of their descendants, even to the tenth generation, shall ever enter the assembly of the LORD." Also consider what Naomi and Ruth had endured over the past ten years in Moab.

What issues do you think Naomi was struggling with?

Trouble will rain on those who are already wet.
—Spanish proverb

Describe what Ruth was giving up and getting into by making the decision she did.

Her family's sojourn in Moab certainly did not turn out as Naomi had planned. She could never have envisioned what took place during those ten years. As you look back in your life, describe a time that was similar, a time when everything turned out differently than you had planned. How did you handle it?

Few can foresee whither their road will lead them, till they come to its end.

—J. R. R. TOLKIEN, English professor and author of THE LORD OF THE RINGS trilogy

In the next lesson we will look at how Naomi handled her situation.

MEMORY VERSE

Blessed is the LORD who has not left you without a redeemer today.

RUTH 4:14

REVIEW IT!
Chapter 1 is the Crucial Chapter because it prepares us for the kinsman redeemer episode.

RUTH
[Redemption Defined]

THINK ABOUT IT
Naomi means
"pleasant." Ruth means
"gracious one."

DAY THREE

COMPLETE READ: Chapters 1–4
QUICK READ: Chapter 2

A PROMINENT PLAYER

George Mueller was a famous British orphanage founder in the nineteenth century. One of the greatest trials of his life was the death of his wife, Mary, of rheumatic fever. They had been married almost forty years, and Mueller was sixty-four when she died. Shortly after her death, he preached what he termed a "funeral sermon." He chose the text of Psalm 119:68, which says of God, "You are good and do good."

He included three points in his sermon:

1. The Lord was good and did good in giving her to him.

2. The Lord was good and did good in giving them so many years together.

3. The Lord was good and did good in taking her from him.

During his wife's illness, he prayed the following prayer:

> Yes, my Father, the times of my darling wife are in Thy hands. Thou wilt do the very best thing for her and for me, whether life or death. If it may be, raise up yet again my precious wife. Thou art able to do it, though she is so ill; but howsoever Thou dealest with me, only help me to continue to be perfectly satisfied with Thy holy will.[4]

The only saving faith is that which casts itself on God for life or death.

—MARTIN LUTHER, sixteenth-century German theologian and reformer

Many times, a trial such as the one Mueller endured produces only bitterness, not trust. Mueller's concentration on the goodness of God gave him strength to endure with victory.

Almost three thousand years earlier, Naomi, serving the same God as George Mueller, experienced a deeper, though similar, trial. Read Ruth 1:19-21 and write down your thoughts to the following questions about our Prominent Player, Naomi, a woman struggling with life's difficulties.

How would you describe Naomi's attitude?

INTERESTING!
Even today, Arab farmers do not harvest the corners of their fields, leaving them for the poor and the foreigners (see Ruth 2:3).

In the previous verses, especially 8-18, what do you see that gives hints of this attitude?

No doubt Ruth also saw this attitude in Naomi. What does this realization add to your thoughts about Ruth's commitment to her in verses 15-18?

I have plumbed the depths of despair and have found them not bottomless.
—Thomas Hardy, English novelist and poet of the nineteenth century

If you had been a friend of Naomi welcoming her back to Bethlehem and heard her say what she did in verses 20-21, how would you have responded to her?

What hints do you pick up in the following passages about Naomi's attitudes?

Ruth 2:17-23

Ruth 4:13-17

Take a few minutes to thank God for His grace in dealing with you as you have worked or are working through attitudes that fall short of holiness.

MEMORY VERSE

Blessed is the LORD who has not left you without a redeemer today.

RUTH 4:14

RUTH
[Redemption Defined]

DAY FOUR

COMPLETE READ: Chapters 1–4
QUICK READ: Chapter 4

DID YOU NOTICE?
The words *redeem*, *buy*, and *purchase* are used at least fifteen times in chapter 4.

A NOTABLE FEATURE

The book of Ruth as a picture of our redemption is not a business or legal transaction. It is a love story. What a great picture for many of us who have become accustomed to thinking of our salvation as a transaction in which God bought us out of the slave market of sin because He had the right price to pay. All of this is true:

- We were slaves to sin and Satan.

- God bought us back out of that market.

- The price was the blood of His only Son.

But the story of Ruth and Boaz reminds us again that the foundation of redemption is God's love for us, as we read in John 3:16: "For God so loved the world, that He gave His only begotten Son." Boaz redeemed both Naomi's property and Ruth because of his love for Ruth. In expressing that love, he fulfilled the law of the kinsman redeemer. The responsibility of the nearest kinsman was to redeem land that a relative was being forced to sell (see Leviticus 25:23-34) and to marry a widowed relative (especially a sister-in-law, but sometimes a more distant relative) in order to raise up offspring for the continuance of her deceased husband's name (see Deuteronomy 25:5-10).

O Love that will not let me go, I rest my weary soul in Thee.

—GEORGE MATHESON,
Scottish theologian and preacher

INSIGHT
The city gate was usually a small building with open rooms so people could easily see what was being done in them.[5]

Read Ruth 4:1-13 and describe in your own words the sequence of events that took place for this kinsman redeemer relationship to occur.

This picture is clearly a visualization on the human level of what Jesus did for us. A kinsman redeemer had to meet certain qualifications before he was considered adequate for this responsibility. Look at the verses below relating to both Boaz and Jesus Christ and write down how both fulfilled each requirement.

	BOAZ	**JESUS**
He had to be a near kinsman.	Ruth 2:1,3,20; 3:12-13	John 1:14 Philippians 2:5-8 Hebrews 2:17
He had to be willing to redeem.	Ruth 2:8; 3:11	Mark 10:45 Luke 19:10
He had to have the price of redemption.	Ruth 2:1; 4:9-10	1 Peter 1:18-19 Hebrews 9:11-14

Jesus Christ is everything for man's total need.

—RICHARD HALVERSON, former chaplain of the U.S. Senate

Our Kinsman Redeemer willingly became a near kinsman by becoming a man and by paying our redemption price through His death on the cross. Why? Because He loved us so deeply. Jesus Himself said, "Greater love has no one than this, that one lay down his life for his friends" (John 15:13).

Take time to write a short prayer of gratitude to your Kinsman Redeemer for the love He showed you when He redeemed you.

Thou hast given so much to me. . . . Give one thing more — a grateful heart.
—GEORGE HERBERT, English clergyman and poet

MEMORY VERSE

Blessed is the LORD who has not left you without a redeemer today.

RUTH 4:14

REVIEW IT!
The Notable Feature of the book of Ruth is the kinsman redeemer concept.

RUTH
[Redemption Defined]

CHECK IT OUT
Ruth 4:17 is the first
mention of David in the
Bible.

DAY FIVE

COMPLETE READ: Chapters 1–4
QUICK READ: Chapter 4

A TIMELESS PRINCIPLE

- Early Christians thrown to the lions because of their faith

- Reformers burned at the stake for refusing to deny Jesus Christ

- Citizens denied common economic rights for holding to their Christian beliefs

- Employees passed over for promotion because they refuse to compromise their ethics

- Neighbors shunned at the neighborhood party because they are "too religious"

Light, even though it passes through pollution, is not polluted.

—SAINT AUGUSTINE OF HIPPO, fourth-century bishop in northern Africa

These are all examples of people standing firm for their Christian convictions in the midst of a world that is going the other way. The apostle Paul put it this way: "And do not be conformed to this world, but be transformed by the renewing of your mind" (Romans 12:2).

In the book of Ruth, the characters shine as bright lights in the darkness of their age. Remember, Ruth 1:1 begins, "Now it came about in the days when the judges governed. . . ." We saw in our study of Judges how bleak and dark and hopeless those days were. Now that you have read the book of Ruth, you can see how different this story is from the days in which it took place — days in which everyone did as he pleased.

Think through the following contrasts:

JUDGES	RUTH
Disloyalty	Loyalty
Unfaithfulness	Faithfulness
Hate	Love
Disobedience	Obedience
Lust	Purity
Cruelty	Kindness
War	Peace
Battlefield	Harvest Field
Dark Sky	Bright Star

Also consider the last verse in Judges: "In those days there was no king in Israel; everyone did what was right in his own eyes" (21:25) and the last verse in Ruth: "And to Obed was born Jesse, and to Jesse, David" (4:22). David was the king who would be described as "a man after God's own heart."

Review the book of Ruth and briefly write down what you see that stands out as a bright star against a very dark sky.

The powers are strong, but Christ is stronger still. The defeat of the powers is sure. We live in that life that overcomes the world.

—RICHARD FOSTER, author of *Celebration of Discipline*

The age in which we live has many positive and beneficial aspects — blessings for which we should be grateful to God. But it also has many dark features that challenge and tempt us.

What are the most difficult challenges in your world? How are you doing in your efforts to face them? Conclude your time with an appropriate prayer for your situation.

Powerful and merciful Savior, keep me from evil today. When I am weak, give me strength; when I am tempted, grant me courage; when I am disheartened, provide me with hope. In the name of Jesus who "himself was tested by what he suffered" (Hebrews 2:18). Amen.

—Eugene Peterson, pastor and author of *A Long Obedience in the Same Direction*

Memory Verse

Blessed is the Lord who has not left you without a redeemer today.

Ruth 4:14

RUTH
[Redemption Defined]

REVIEW

1. The theme of Ruth is living out the law of the kinsman _____ .

2. Chapter _____ is the Crucial Chapter because it prepares us for the kinsman redeemer episode.

3. Our Prominent Player is _____ because of her struggle with bitterness in the light of life's difficulties.

4. The Notable Feature of the book of Ruth is the _____ redeemer concept.

5. "Blessed is the LORD who has not left you without a _____ today."

RUTH 4:_____

I SAMUEL

[*Monarchy Established*]

Man looks at the outward appearance,

but the LORD *looks at the heart.*

I SAMUEL 16:7

FOUR

I SAMUEL
[Monarchy Established]

INTRODUCTION

First Samuel begins chronologically where the book of Judges leaves off. The nation was morally bankrupt, and even the priests were corrupt. This book provides an inside look at the rise of the monarchy in Israel through the story of three men.

Samuel was dedicated to God from infancy and served Him with passion all the days of his life. He was a prophet, a judge, and a priest. When the people demanded a king, Samuel tried to dissuade them. Despite his attempts, Israel's first king was appointed, and the period of judges came to an end.

Saul, Israel's first king, was a complex man. Samuel anointed Saul and tried to lead him in the ways of God, and in his youth Saul showed great potential. But as he grew older, he became obsessed with doing things his own way and controlling that which could be controlled only by God. Saul's jealousy toward young David began a mental and emotional downward spiral, which eventually led Israel to near destruction and turned Saul's heart away from God.

The nation's second king, David, was also anointed by Samuel. Even in youth, David showed remarkable faith and confidence in God. His skill as a shepherd, warrior, and leader won him the love and devotion of the people.

I SAMUEL
[Monarchy Established]

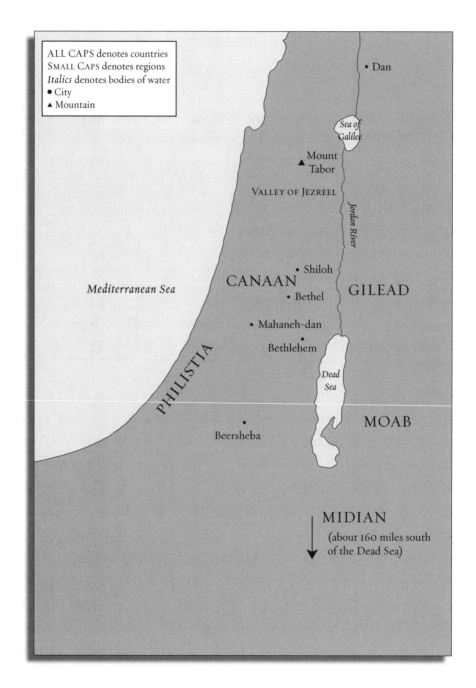

ALL CAPS denotes countries
SMALL CAPS denotes regions
Italics denotes bodies of water
• City
▲ Mountain

• Dan

Sea of Galilee

▲ Mount Tabor

VALLEY OF JEZREEL

Jordan River

Mediterranean Sea

CANAAN

• Shiloh

• Bethel

GILEAD

• Mahaneh-dan

• Bethlehem

Dead Sea

PHILISTIA

•
Beersheba

MOAB

MIDIAN
(about 160 miles south
of the Dead Sea)

I SAMUEL
[Monarchy Established]

OVERVIEW

WHO: Author: Most likely Samuel
Main Characters: Samuel, Saul, David

WHAT: "Give us a king!"—Israel becomes a monarchy

WHEN: Covers 94 years—from the birth of Samuel, the last judge (1105 BC), to the death of Saul, the first king (1011 BC)

WHERE: Canaan

WHY: Israel's theocracy becomes a monarchy when the people demand a king

I. THE LIFE OF SAMUEL (1 SAMUEL 1–8)

A. Hannah trusted God and He gave her a son, Samuel.

B. Eli, the unfaithful priest, raised Samuel from the time he was weaned.

C. Samuel's offices included:

   1. He was Israel's last and most effective _____ .

   2. He was Israel's first _____ .

   3. He served as a _____ .

D. He was chosen by God for these offices.

E. He sought God's guidance through prayer all his life.

II. THE REIGN OF SAUL (1 SAMUEL 9–15)

A. Saul was Israel's _____ king.

B. Saul was anointed by Samuel but chosen by _____ .

C. Saul was disqualified by God for his _____ .

D. He sought guidance from a _____ and not from God.

E. Saul _____ after forty years as king of Israel.

Ch 16

III. **The Faithfulness of David, God's Chosen King (1 Samuel 16–31)**

    A. David was anointed as Israel's king *elect* .

    B. He was anointed by Samuel but chosen by *God* .

    C. He was qualified to be king by his *faithfulness* .

    D. David sought *God* and lived.

    E. David trusted God and killed the Philistine *giant* , Goliath.

    F. There was an ongoing conflict between *man's* king, Saul, and *God's* king, David.

    G. David had a covenant relationship with Saul's son Jonathan.

Application

Jesus is the King of kings. Is He reigning as King over your life, or are you demanding another king?

I SAMUEL
[Monarchy Established]

LEARNING FOR LIFE

1. Beginning with the book of Joshua, give an overview of the history of Israel (group effort).

2. The people of Israel demanded a king. What was their reason? What are some of the things that God said would happen if they had a king? (See 1 Samuel 8:11-18.)

3. Are you ruled by a king? What is His name? (See Zechariah 9:9; Matthew 21:1-5.)

4. What are some of the mistakes Saul made as king? What character weakness do his actions imply?

5. Describe each of the following characters, tell how they fit into the book of 1 Samuel, and explain what their relationship to God was: Samuel, Saul, Jonathan, and David.

I SAMUEL
[Monarchy Established]

DAY ONE

COMPLETE READ: Chapters 1–7
QUICK READ: Chapters 1–3

THE BIG PICTURE

The grass is always greener on the other side of the fence.

We know this famous phrase speaks of the discontent of human nature. In so many ways, we are never satisfied, and we think others have it better than we do. But even though logic tells us that everyone feels this way, something deep down in our hearts still believes that the grass is truly greener on the other side of the fence.

The Israelites, as individual people and collectively as a nation, were no different than we are today. In the book of 1 Samuel, Israel looked around and saw something other nations had that they did not — and they wanted it.

As a result, the book of 1 Samuel describes a transition time in the life of God's chosen people, the nation of Israel. Up until this point they had been a theocracy, directly under the rule of God. But in 1 Samuel, as we will see in our Crucial Chapter, they asked God to give them a king just as the other nations had. This led them from a theocracy to a monarchy, and the transition was more difficult than they could ever have dreamed.

The books of 1 and 2 Samuel were originally one book known as The Book of Samuel or simply Samuel. It was divided into two books when the Septuagint, the Greek translation of the Old Testament, was written in the second to third centuries BC.

Covetousness is a self-destructive passion, a craving which is never satisfied, even when what has been craved is now possessed.

—JOHN STOTT, author and Christian leader

We do not know for certain who authored this book. Though the book bears the name of Samuel, he could not have written it in its entirety because chapter 25 records his death. He most likely contributed the early parts of the book, while others completed it. The book covers a period of 94 years from the birth of Samuel around 1105 BC to the death of Saul in 1011 BC. Samuel died in 1015 BC at the age of ninety.

The book of 1 Samuel can be divided into three major parts:

Samuel: The Last Judge	Saul: The First King	Saul & David: The First King and King Elect
1 8	9 15	16 31

As the chart shows, the three principal characters of the book are Samuel, Saul, and David. The Quick Read for today records the birth and early development of Samuel, one of the most significant characters in the Old Testament. Write down any thoughts or insights you had about Samuel from your reading today.

IMPORTANT
As you read Hannah's prayer, remember that to be childless in Near Eastern cultures was also considered a mark of divine judgment.

We mostly spend [our] lives conjugating three verbs: to Want, to Have, and to Do. Craving, clutching, and fussing, we are kept in perpetual unrest, forgetting that none of these verbs have any ultimate significance. Being, not wanting, having and doing, is the essence of a spiritual life.
—EVELYN UNDERHILL, prolific English writer on the spiritual life

The three main actors in the drama called 1 Samuel will have much to teach us about character, both positive and negative. Be on the lookout for these important insights as you read this week.

REVIEW IT!
The theme of 1 Samuel is "Give us a king!"— Israel becomes a monarchy.

MEMORY VERSE

Man looks at the outward appearance, but the LORD looks at the heart.

1 SAMUEL 16:7

I SAMUEL
[Monarchy Established]

DAY TWO

COMPLETE READ: Chapters 8–13

QUICK READ: Chapter 8

NOTE
The phrase "the LORD
of hosts" appears for
the first time in the
Bible in 1 Samuel 1:3.

A CRUCIAL CHAPTER

All parents at some point warn their child not to touch something when it is hot. And almost every child, even when he's been warned, ends up touching it to find out for himself. And then he gets burned.

A similar encounter is recorded in our Crucial Chapter, 1 Samuel 8. The people became frustrated over ungodly leadership and were jealous of the nations around them, so they asked for a king to rule them. Samuel warned them that they would get burned — a king would not bring them what they expected. They demanded one anyway — and they did get burned.

Read 1 Samuel 8:1-9, Act I of this drama. Summarize in your own words what takes place here.

*It is what we think
we know already
that prevents us from
learning.*

—CLAUDE BERNARD,
nineteenth-century
French physiologist

Read Act II of this drama, verses 10-18, and describe the elements of the warning Samuel gave the people to dissuade them from desiring a king.

Try to describe in one sentence the kind of environment a king would create for the people.

Read verses 19-22, Act III of this drama, and describe in your own words the emotions that the following actors in the drama must have felt:

The people:

Truth which is merely told is quick to be forgotten; truth which is discovered lasts a lifetime.

—WILLIAM BARCLAY,
sixteenth-century
Scottish jurist

Samuel:

The Lord:

From this point on, everything changed for the people. Many of the warnings of "what could be" became reality. Eventually, because of the great sins of the king and of the people as they followed his example, the nation endured the discipline of God as He employed a foreign nation to take them captive. The people thought that what they wanted was right and the best thing for them. It wasn't. They did not heed the warning.

Have you ever gotten burned after doing something that you had been warned ahead of time would only cause pain and hardship? Describe it briefly.

The gospel has a life of its own, and does its slow, steady work regardless.
—Philip Yancey, author of *What's So Amazing About Grace?*

Considering that God uses all things to work together for our good (see Romans 8:28), what benefit did you gain from that negative experience? (Examples might be increased character, a bigger picture of God, or a truer picture of yourself.)

MEMORY VERSE

Man looks at the outward appearance, but the LORD looks at the heart.

1 SAMUEL 16:7

REVIEW IT!
Chapter 8 is the Crucial Chapter because it is the bridge that moves Israel from a theocracy to a monarchy.

I SAMUEL
[Monarchy Established]

DID YOU KNOW?
The strange but familiar names Ebenezer and Ichabod occur in 1 Samuel (7:12 and 4:21).

DAY THREE

COMPLETE READ: Chapters 14–19
QUICK READ: Chapters 9–11

A PROMINENT PLAYER, PART 1

At graduation time every year, everyone wonders — and guesses — who, of all the graduates, will most likely succeed. Wouldn't it be interesting to know how many times those we think will succeed don't? We likely would be shocked by how often we are wrong.

It is so easy to *look* successful at the beginning. It is an entirely different thing to *be* successful at the end.

In the beginning, Israel's first king, Saul, looked very good. He had achievement, success, and victory written all over him. In today's study, we will look at the promise of his success. Tomorrow, we will study the rest of Saul's story and discover that he never realized his potential.

The two hardest things to handle in life are failure and success.

—Unknown

Read 1 Samuel 9:1-10 and list all the positive traits (physical, emotional, attitudinal) about Saul that you can find. If necessary, explain how the trait is shown.

What impresses you about Saul in 1 Samuel 9:18-21?

How is Saul's potential evidenced in 1 Samuel 10:1-13?

INTERESTING!
The first biblical use of
"Long live the king!"
occurs in
1 Samuel 10:24.

Again in 1 Samuel 10:17-24, Saul displays character traits that give significant hope that he will be a successful king. What traits do you see in these verses?

Finally, in 1 Samuel 11:1-15, Saul exhibits additional qualities that are admirable. Describe what you see in this passage.

When you pull together everything you have learned about Saul, how would you describe him, and what chance of success would you assign to him?

It is not your business to succeed, but to do right; when you have done so, the rest lies with God.

—C. S. Lewis, author of
The Chronicles of Narnia

What positive traits do you see in yourself that promise potential yet to be realized? After listing them, thank God for them and ask Him to bear fruit for Himself through those qualities in you.

REVIEW IT!
Saul is a Prominent Player because he had all the makings of a great king.

MEMORY VERSE

Man looks at the outward appearance, but the LORD looks at the heart.

1 SAMUEL 16:7

I SAMUEL
[Monarchy Established]

DAY FOUR

COMPLETE READ: Chapters 20–25
QUICK READ: Chapters 13 and 15

INTERESTING!
Many scholars believe
that Samuel formed a
school of the prophets
(1 Samuel 10:5; 19:20).

A PROMINENT PLAYER, PART 2

In the diamond mines of South Africa, a substance is often found that is half-charcoal and half-diamond. For some unknown reason, this substance never fulfills its intended purpose. It is never set in a king's crown or a bride's ring. In its developmental state, the substance failed to become what it might have been.

Look at 1 Samuel 15:1-23. What sins do you see in this passage that disqualified Saul from his privileged role?

Men are often capable of greater things than they perform. They are sent into the world with bills of credit, and seldom draw to their full extent.

—HORACE WALPOLE,
eighteenth-century
English author

1 Samuel 28:3-19 describes a further disintegration of Saul's character. Describe what Saul did and why he did it.

CHECK IT OUT
The first chapter of
1 Samuel and the last
chapter of 2 Samuel
center on prayer.

Briefly jot down words or phrases you would use to describe the Saul of today's study.

When you compare the Saul of yesterday's study with the Saul of this study, what thoughts and feelings do you have?

Our chief want is someone who will inspire us to be what we know we could be.
—RALPH WALDO EMERSON, nineteenth-century American essayist and poet

Do you know a modern-day Saul — a person who had extraordinary promise but never became all he or she could have become? Briefly describe that person's situation.

Is it possible that you have areas of your life that are Saul-like — half-charcoal and half-diamond — that will never reach their potential unless you ask God to intervene? Will you repent of whatever might be holding you back and ask Him to forgive your shortcomings and rebuild this area of your life in His time and in His way?

REVIEW IT!
Saul is a Prominent Player because his weaknesses overcame his strengths and caused him to sin and lose his kingship.

MEMORY VERSE

Man looks at the outward appearance, but the LORD looks at the heart.

1 SAMUEL 16:7

I SAMUEL
[Monarchy Established]

AMAZING!
The word *heart*,
referring to the inner
life, occurs over eight
hundred times in
the Bible!

DAY FIVE

COMPLETE READ: Chapters 26–31
QUICK READ: Chapter 16:1-13

A TIMELESS PRINCIPLE

> Watch over your *heart* with all diligence, for from it flow the springs of life.
>
> —PROVERBS 4:23

> As in water face reflects face, so the *heart* of man reflects man.
>
> —PROVERBS 27:19

> The *heart* is more deceitful than all else and is desperately sick; who can understand it?
>
> —JEREMIAH 17:9

> For out of the *heart* come evil thoughts, murders, adulteries, fornications, thefts, false witness, slanders.
>
> —MATTHEW 15:19

> You shall love the Lord your God with all your *heart*, and with all your soul, and with all your mind.
>
> —MATTHEW 22:37

> But let it [your adornment] be the hidden person of the *heart*, with the imperishable quality of a gentle and quiet spirit.
>
> —I PETER 3:4

What lies behind us and what lies before us are tiny matters compared to what lies within us.

—RALPH WALDO EMERSON, nineteenth-century American essayist and poet

Our Timeless Principle—"Man looks at the outward appearance, but the LORD looks at the heart"—is taken from the Memory Verse for I Samuel, 16:7. It's a powerful verse—and even more powerful when read in the company of the above verses (italics all for emphasis).

Without delving into all the theological nuances of the nature of man, it is safe to say that our heart is the controlling center of our life. It is the core of our being, our soul, and our character. It is the headwaters of our motives and behaviors. It is the source of our ideas, beliefs, feelings, habits, tendencies, actions, outlook, and choices. And it is astonishingly complex, subtle, and even devious. We kid ourselves if we think we have it mastered.

Even secular author Kevin Cashman writes, "I think the reason most people think they know themselves well is that their experience of their inner world is restricted to very narrow boundaries."[1] In his book *Let Your Life Speak,* Parker Palmer says, "We like to talk about the outer world as if it were infinitely complex and demanding, but it is a cakewalk compared to the labyrinth of our inner lives."[2]

It is this inner life, this core of our being — our heart — that God looks at. We see it sometimes. Our friends see it sometimes. But God sees it always. And His desire for us is that with His help, we would tend it very carefully.

Consider this thought from Dallas Willard. He writes in *Renovation of the Heart,*

> The revolution of Jesus is in the first place and continuously a revolution of the human heart or spirit. It did not and does not proceed by means of the formation of social institutions and laws, the outer forms of our existence, intending that these would then impose a good order of life upon people who come under their power. Rather, his is a revolution of *character,* which proceeds by changing people from the inside through ongoing personal relationship to God in Christ and to one another. . . . External, social arrangements may be useful to this end, but they are not the end, nor are they a fundamental part of the means.[3]

In light of what you've read in the last few minutes, respond to the following questions.

IMPORTANT
God called David "a man after My heart" (Acts 13:22).

Never say you know the last word about any human heart.
—HENRY JAMES, American novelist and literary critic

What do you think God, you, and other people share in understanding about your heart?

What do only God and you know about your heart?

What do you sense God may know about your heart that you only vaguely understand or have only a slight hint about?

In Psalm 139:23-24 David wrote,

> Search me, O God, and know my heart;
> Try me and know my anxious thoughts;
> And see if there be any hurtful way in me,
> And lead me in the everlasting way.

Are you willing to pray these words regularly for a number of days and record what God reveals to you about your heart? If so, begin right now.

Without grace I would be letting these thoughts, this pesty swarm of flies, as William of Saint Thierry calls them, spoil the sweetness of the ointment, the devotion of mind and heart. How completely we are dependent on the coming and abiding presence of His grace.

—M. BASIL PENNINGTON, author and abbot of the Abbey of Blessed Mary of Saint Joseph

MEMORY VERSE

Man looks at the outward appearance, but the LORD looks at the heart.

1 SAMUEL 16:7

I SAMUEL
[Monarchy Established]

REVIEW

1. The theme of I Samuel is "Give us a _____!"—Israel becomes a monarchy.

2. Chapter 8 is the Crucial Chapter because it is the bridge that moves Israel from a theocracy to a _____ .

3. _____ is a Prominent Player because he had all the makings of a great king.

4. Saul is a Prominent Player because his _____ overcame his strengths and caused him to sin and lose his kingship.

5. "Man looks at the outward appearance, but the LORD looks at the _____ ."

I SAMUEL 16:_____

2 SAMUEL

[David's Throne Established]

May the house of Your servant David

be established before You.

2 SAMUEL 7:26

FIVE

2 SAMUEL
[David's Throne Established]

INTRODUCTION

First Samuel ends with the death of Saul and the nation of Israel in great turmoil. In 2 Samuel, David returned to the tribe of Judah and ruled as their king for the next seven years. During this time, Saul's son reigned as king over the northern ten tribes. Upon his death, all of Israel asked David to be their king. Under David's capable leadership, Israel was strongly united and victorious in every battle.

Second Samuel is the history of David's reign as king and covers about forty years. Watch David, and you will see a man who loved God passionately, humbled Himself under God's authority, and was a man after God's own heart — yet still he sinned. The success of his life was tarnished but not erased by the sorrows of his sin.

2 SAMUEL
[David's Throne Established]

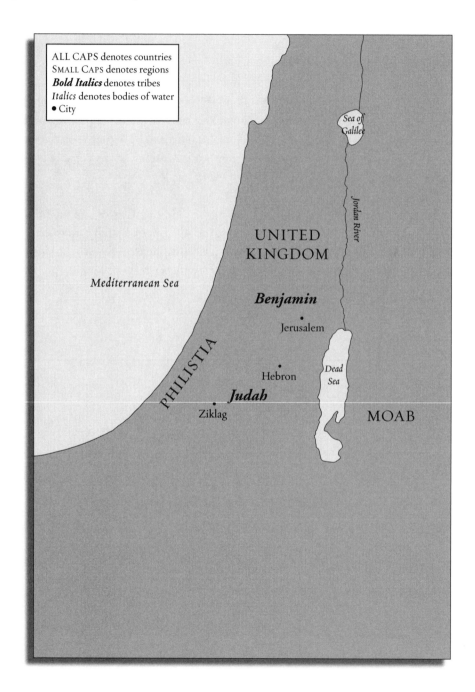

ALL CAPS denotes countries
SMALL CAPS denotes regions
Bold Italics denotes tribes
Italics denotes bodies of water
● City

Sea of Galilee

Jordan River

UNITED KINGDOM

Mediterranean Sea

Benjamin
●
Jerusalem

Dead Sea

●
Hebron

Judah
●
Ziklag

PHILISTIA

MOAB

2 SAMUEL
[David's Throne Established]

OVERVIEW

WHO: Author: Uncertain
Main Character: David

WHAT: David establishes the monarchy

WHEN: The book covers forty years (1011–971 BC)

WHERE: In chapters 1–4, David is king over Judah. In chapters 5–24, David is king over all the tribes in one nation (Israel)

WHY: Through David's leadership, all the tribes of Israel were united into one great nation

I. DAVID _____ IN UNITING THE TWELVE TRIBES OF ISRAEL (2 SAMUEL 1–10).

   A. David ruled only one tribe, _____, for seven years.

   B. David _____ the twelve tribes after the death of Saul's son.

      1. He established _____ as the capital of Israel (2 Samuel 5).

      2. He established a strong _____ order (2 Samuel 6).

      3. He expanded the _____ of Israel (2 Samuel 8–10).

      4. God made a _____ with King David (2 Samuel 7).

II. DAVID _____ AGAINST GOD (2 SAMUEL 11–12).

   A. David committed _____ with Bathsheba.

   B. David _____ Uriah.

   C. The prophet _____ confronted David with his sin.

   D. David _____ and repented of his sin before God.

III. DAVID SUFFERED _____*troubles*_____ FROM THE CONSEQUENCES OF HIS SIN (2 SAMUEL 13–21).

A. David's infant _____*son*_____ died (2 Samuel 12).

B. David's son Amnon _____*seduced*_____ his half sister Tamar and then raped her (2 Samuel 13).

C. Tamar's brother Absalom _____*murdered*_____ Amnon.

D. Absalom led a _____*revolt*_____ against his father, David (2 Samuel 15–18).

E. Absalom was _____*murdered*_____ by David's army commander.

IV. DAVID TESTIFIED TO THE FAITHFULNESS OF GOD (2 SAMUEL 22–24).

A. In success, he praised God.

B. In sin, he repented before God.

C. In sorrow, he clung to God.

D. He was a man after God's own heart.

APPLICATION

God can be trusted in our triumphs, will forgive us for our transgressions, and will strengthen and encourage us in our troubles.

2 SAMUEL
[David's Throne Established]

LEARNING FOR LIFE

1. Review The Kingdom Books from Joshua through 2 Samuel (group effort).

2. What are some of the important events that take place in 2 Samuel?

3. What were some of the consequences of David's sin?

4. David was called a man after God's own heart. Describe someone you know or know about who would fit that description today.

5. What is the connection between King David and Jesus Christ? (See Matthew 1:1; Luke 1:26-33.)

6. David praised God in success, in sin, and in sorrow. Which one of these three words describes where you are today? What can you learn from David's response to God?

2 SAMUEL
[David's Throne Established]

JUST A THOUGHT
Do you think any passage of the Bible is as widely known as that of Psalm 23?

DAY ONE

COMPLETE READ: Chapters 1–5
QUICK READ: Chapters 1–2

THE BIG PICTURE

The Lord is my shepherd, that's all I want.

—Small child, misquoting Psalm 23

The LORD is my shepherd,
I shall not want.
He makes me lie down in green pastures;
He leads me beside quiet waters.
He restores my soul;
He guides me in the paths of righteousness
For His name's sake.
Even though I walk through the valley of the shadow
 of death,
I fear no evil, for You are with me;
Your rod and Your staff, they comfort me.
You prepare a table before me in the presence of my
 enemies;
You have anointed my head with oil;
My cup overflows.
Surely goodness and lovingkindness will follow me all
 the days of my life,
And I will dwell in the house of the LORD forever.

—PSALM 23

These are probably the most well-known words of the entire Bible. David, the author, was one of the most multitalented individuals to ever live. He was a shepherd, a musician, a poet, a warrior, a general, and a king. And if there is one book that portrays

David's character development, it is the book of 2 Samuel. His story begins in 1 Samuel, but it is in 2 Samuel that he is the sole human in the spotlight.

As you follow David's character in 2 Samuel, keep the message of Psalm 23 in your mind and from time to time pick out a phrase that you think would apply the most to David at that moment in his story.

As you learned in our study of 1 Samuel, the two books of 1 and 2 Samuel were originally one, but the scholars who translated the Old Testament into Greek during the second and third centuries BC divided them. Therefore, the book of 2 Samuel picks up right where 1 Samuel left off: at the death of Saul in 1011 BC. Second Samuel ends very near the time of David's death in 971 BC as recorded in chapters 1 and 2 of 1 Kings.

Soon after the death of Saul, David, the king elect, became the king enthroned. He reigned in Hebron for the first seven and a half years and then in Jerusalem for the remaining thirty-three years. The book of 2 Samuel records his forty-year reign.

Because David is the central character of the book, the events of his life form the major divisions of the book, as shown in the following chart.

No wonder we find so much in David to admire and so much we wish we could ignore.
—Reggie McNeal, author of *A Work of Heart*

Triumphs of David	Transgressions of David	Troubles of David	Testimony of David
1 10	11 12	13 21	22 24

As we learned in the last five lessons, 1 Samuel describes how the nation transitioned into a monarchy. In the five lessons of 2 Samuel, we'll see how David, the second king, established Israel as a power. David's accomplishments in establishing the nation include:

- Unifying the nation

- Obtaining and establishing a royal capital

- Subduing Israel's enemies

- Extending the country's boundaries

- Creating a national consciousness

- Bringing prosperity by extending trade

The author of the book of 2 Samuel is unknown. Most likely it was compiled by one man using the written records of Nathan the prophet and Gad the seer (see 1 Chronicles 29:29) sometime soon after the death of David.

Second Samuel affords us a more intimate look at David's actions, failures, innermost thoughts, and emotions than any other book about any other character in Scripture. As you read, you may find it easy to identify with David as a human being who, just like you, sought to walk with God in a way that was authentic and faithful. Consider keeping a brief journal of thoughts you have about *your* life as a result of reading *his* life.

REVIEW IT!
The theme of 2 Samuel is David establishes the monarchy.

Memory Verse

May the house of Your servant David be established before You.

2 Samuel 7:26

2 Samuel: Day One

2 SAMUEL
[David's Throne Established]

DAY TWO

COMPLETE READ: Chapters 6–10
QUICK READ: Chapter 7

A CRUCIAL CHAPTER

We are all familiar with a contract — an agreement between two parties, each of whom accepts responsibility for certain parts of the agreement. In our time, most people negotiate contracts by:

- Seeking as little responsibility as possible

- Realizing that distrust is implicit in the agreement

- Attempting to ensure that by mutual consent it can be made null and void

God does not negotiate contracts. He institutes covenants, both conditional and unconditional. And when He initiates an unconditional covenant with the words "I will" and without any "ifs," we can be certain He will carry the covenant to fulfillment.

In 2 Samuel 7, our Crucial Chapter (and also our Quick Read for today), God institutes the Davidic covenant, the beginning of an endless dynasty of kings. Because it is an unconditional covenant instituted by God, we can be certain that every provision will be carried out. The covenant with David is described in 2 Samuel 7:8-16 and includes promises to be fulfilled during David's lifetime and after his death.

DURING DAVID'S LIFETIME
Read the following promises and look up the passages that show their fulfillment.

IMPORTANT
The Davidic covenant was not the last covenant. The last covenant God instituted was the New Covenant prophesied by Jeremiah and fulfilled by Jesus Christ.

Lord, I am no longer my own, but Yours. So be it. Amen.
—JOHN WESLEY, founder of Methodism

PROMISE	**FULFILLMENT**
1. "I will make you a great name" (7:9).	2 Samuel 8:13-14
2. "I will also appoint a place for My people Israel" (7:10).	2 Samuel 8:3 (referring to the Euphrates River)
3. "I will give you rest from all your enemies" (7:11).	1 Kings 5:1-4; 1 Chronicles 22:6-9

So in David's lifetime, God made his name great, He set the boundaries for the land of Israel, and He gave Israel rest from all its enemies. But the remainder of the covenant's promises extended far beyond David's lifetime. They are summarized below.

AFTER DAVID'S DEATH
1. "I will raise up your descendant [literally: seed] after you" (7:12). This doesn't refer only to Solomon but to a royal seed from the line of David continuing down through the years. Read Psalm 89:3-4,20-37. What do these verses tell you about this covenant in 2 Samuel 7?

The main hinge on which faith turns is this: we must not imagine that the Lord's promises are true objectively but not in our experience. We must make them ours by embracing them in our hearts.

—JOHN CALVIN, French Protestant reformer and theologian

2. "Your kingdom shall endure before Me forever" (7:16). Not only will there always be a king in the line of David but there will also be a kingdom for him to rule.

3. "I will be a father to him and he will be a son to Me" (7:14). Every king following David will be adopted as a son of God, and God will discipline him as needed. The only King who will never be disciplined is Jesus Christ — the last king in the line of David who will reign forever over an eternal kingdom from the power of an eternal throne.

After David received this amazing set of promises, he could not help but break out in praise, adoration, and thanksgiving to

God. Read his prayer in 7:18-29 and record any thoughts or feelings you have as you read it.

In a way that is meaningful to you, thank God that His Son fulfilled the ultimate promise of the Davidic covenant by becoming the forever King.

Memory Verse

May the house of Your servant David be established before You.

2 Samuel 7:26

REVIEW IT!
Chapter 7 is our Crucial Chapter because in it, God institutes the Davidic covenant.

2 SAMUEL
[David's Throne Established]

NOTE
Israel's first three kings each reigned for forty years.

DAY THREE

COMPLETE READ: Chapters 11–15
QUICK READ: Chapter 6

A PROMINENT PLAYER

Certain people set the standard. In their life, work, and service, they raise the bar of what can be. Think of Mother Teresa for commitment. Martin Luther for conviction. Corrie ten Boom for courage. Jesus for forgiveness. Van Gogh for creativity. Helen Keller for overcoming physical challenges. Michael Jordan for athletic prowess. Golda Meir for leadership. And the list goes on.

But no list would be complete without David, the shepherd son of Jesse. He set the standard for kings. In fact, all other kings were judged by him. Read, for example, 2 Chronicles 28:1 and 29:1-2. But the standard he set goes far beyond his abilities and actions as king. Read what is recorded of him in Acts 13:22: "After He had removed him [Saul], He raised up David to be their king, concerning whom He also testified and said, 'I have found David the son of Jesse, a man after My heart, who will do all My will.'"

Let's look at a few vignettes from the life of the man described by God as "a man after My heart" in order to discover some of the traits that made him that kind of man, that kind of standard.

He is truly great who is little in his own eyes and makes nothing of the highest honor.

—THOMAS À KEMPIS, fifteenth-century Augustine monk and author of *The Imitation of Christ*

Read 2 Samuel 1, which describes David's reaction to the death of Saul. As you read, remember the incredible turmoil Saul had caused for David while he was alive. What does David's response to Saul's death in this chapter say about this man after God's heart?

DID YOU KNOW?
David is a descendant of Ruth (see Ruth 4:17,22).

Your Quick Read for today, 2 Samuel 6, tells about David moving the ark of God to Jerusalem and the interesting reaction of his wife Michal to his exuberance. What does this unique chapter tell you about this man after God's heart?

Go back to chapter 30 in the book of 1 Samuel for a different kind of example from David's life. Summarize the three or four most important traits you discovered from reading this story of a man after God's heart.

Jesus taught that a disciple has to make his relationship to God the dominating concentration of his life, and to be carefully careless about everything else in comparison to that.
—OSWALD CHAMBERS, author and missionary

If you have time, go back once more to the book of 1 Samuel and read chapter 26, which pictures additional traits of this man after God's heart. What do you find there?

Which trait most impacted you from these stories? Why?

What one step should you now take to continue moving along in the journey after God's heart?

MEMORY VERSE

May the house of Your servant David be established before You.

2 SAMUEL 7:26

2 SAMUEL
[David's Throne Established]

DAY FOUR

COMPLETE READ: Chapters 16–20
QUICK READ: Chapter 22

NOTE
A good portion of
David's life is recorded
again in the book of 1
Chronicles.

A NOTABLE FEATURE

In his book *The World's Last Night: And Other Essays*, C. S. Lewis writes,

> In getting a dog out of a trap, in extracting a thorn from a child's finger, in teaching a boy to swim or rescuing one who can't, in getting a frightened beginner over a nasty place on a mountain, the one fatal obstacle may be their distrust. . . . We are asking them to believe that what is painful will relieve their pain and that what looks dangerous is their only safety. We ask them to accept apparent impossibilities: that moving the paw farther back into the trap is the way to get out — that hurting the finger very much more will stop the finger hurting — that water which is obviously permeable will resist and support the body . . . that to go higher and onto a more exposed ledge is the way not to fall. To support all these *incredibilia* we can rely only on the other party's confidence in us. . . . Sometimes, because of their unbelief, we can do no mighty works. But if we succeed, we do so because they have maintained their faith in us against apparently contrary evidence. No one blames us for demanding such faith. No one blames them for giving it. No one says afterwards what an unintelligent dog or child or boy that must have been to trust us. . . . Now to accept the Christian propositions is *ipso facto* to believe that we are to God, always, as that dog or child

The saint never knows the joy of the Lord in spite of tribulation, but because of it.

—OSWALD CHAMBERS,
author and missionary

or bather or mountain climber was to us, only very much
more so.[1]

If ever anyone felt like "that dog or child or bather or mountain
climber," it was David. Over and over throughout his life he felt
trapped, experienced pain, thought he was drowning, or didn't
know which scary step to take next. But when he looked back
on it all, he realized how well guarded his faith had been — not
because of his efforts but because of the trustworthiness and
power of the One in whom he had placed his faith.

Chapter 22, our Quick Read for today, records David's attempt
to celebrate the God in whom he had placed his hope — even in
life-and-death situations. The resulting picture shows a God who
is awesome and faithful. As you meditate on this chapter and
respond to the following questions, ask God to show you exactly
what you need to see today about Him and about yourself.

List as many descriptions or pictures of God from this chapter
as you would like (example: "The Lord is my rock").

*"Lo I am with you
always, even unto the
end of the world."* On
these words I staked
everything, and they
never failed.

—DAVID LIVINGSTONE,
Scottish explorer and
missionary in Africa

Now take two or three of these descriptions and write out what
they mean to you personally.

According to David, what were his actions in these encounters with God (example: "I called upon the LORD")?

What are some of the specific things God did in answer to David's pleas (example: "He heard my voice")?

What are two or three of the strongest impressions this poetic chapter had on you? Put into words to God whatever seems appropriate for you at this moment.

MEMORY VERSE

May the house of Your servant David be established before You.

2 SAMUEL 7:26

REVIEW IT!
Chapter 22 is a Notable Feature because it pictures the awesomeness of God in the midst of our trials.

2 SAMUEL
[David's Throne Established]

THINK ABOUT IT
If David, a man after God's heart, could sin, we ought to take warning!

DAY FIVE

COMPLETE READ: Chapters 21–24
QUICK READ: Chapters 11:1–12:13

A TIMELESS PRINCIPLE

In his book *Life-Defining Moments*, James Emery White writes,

> One of the most honest statements I've ever read was from French thinker Joseph de Maistre, who said, "I do not know what the heart of a rascal may be; I know what is in the heart of an honest man; it is horrible." Or as Alexander Whyte said to a woman who praised him for his many good deeds: "Madam, if you knew the man I really was, you would spit in my face." He wasn't confessing to hypocrisy; he was pointing out the reality of human depravity.[2]

Even David, the ideal king and a man after God's heart, experienced the awful consequences of this reality. Most people are familiar with the David and Bathsheba episode. You read the record of it in our Quick Read for today.

In your own words, summarize the flow of events beginning in 2 Samuel 11:1 and ending in 2 Samuel 12:13.

To do so no more is the truest repentance.

—MARTIN LUTHER, German theologian and religious reformer

This narrative simply assumes repentance by David in 12:13. But in God's grace and as instruction for us in this critical area of life, He has recorded David's prayer of repentance in Psalm 51. David's experience as a contrite sinner before God illustrates the two critical components involved in the forgiveness process: genuine repentance and joyful restoration.

GENUINE REPENTANCE (PSALM 51:1-6,16-17)
Read the above verses and respond to the following questions.

On what did David base his hope of forgiveness? Explain.

How would you describe David's attitude in this prayer? Illustrate your descriptions.

Verses 16-17 contain a foundational truth. How would you explain it in your own words?

JOYFUL RESTORATION (PSALM 51:7-15)
Read the above verses and respond to the following questions.

Describe the difference in tone between these verses and the verses of genuine repentance.

The house of my soul is too small for you to come to it. May it be enlarged by you. It is in ruins, restore it.
—SAINT AUGUSTINE OF HIPPO, early church bishop and theologian

What did it mean to David to be restored?

God always promises full forgiveness and restoration following genuine repentance. But He doesn't promise to remove the consequences. The nail hammered into the board (sin) can be removed (repentance and forgiveness), but the hole (consequences) remains.

Read 2 Samuel 12:9-18 and 2 Samuel 13. Describe the consequences David had to live with because of his sin (these are only some of them).

What new thoughts have you had about our Timeless Principle—that genuine repentance brings forgiveness and restoration but not necessarily the removal of consequences? How should you respond to these new insights?

The Greek word for repentance is metanoia. *It simply means "to turn." . . . If a man left the house and then remembered he had forgotten something, he would "repent," turn around and go back home. . . . The biblical call to repent and be converted still essentially means to turn toward the work God is doing in our lives.*

—CRAIG BARNES, *When God Interrupts*

MEMORY VERSE

May the house of Your servant David be established before You.

2 SAMUEL 7:26

2 SAMUEL
[*David's Throne Established*]

REVIEW

1. The theme of 2 Samuel is David establishes the _____ .

2. Chapter 7 is our Crucial Chapter because in it, God institutes the _____ covenant.

3. Our Prominent Player is _____, a man after God's heart.

4. Chapter 22 is a Notable Feature because it pictures the awesomeness of _____ in the midst of our trials.

5. "May the house of Your servant _____ be established before You."

2 SAMUEL 7:_____

I KINGS

[Kingdom Divided]

For when Solomon was old, his wives turned

his heart away after other gods.

<small>1 Kings 11:4</small>

Six

I KINGS
[Kingdom Divided]

INTRODUCTION

After the successful reign of King David in which Israel was united, the throne was passed to David's son Solomon. Though God gave him wisdom, power, and riches beyond comprehension, in his later years Solomon still turned to other gods. His son Rehoboam succeeded his father to the throne, and his foolishness led to a civil dispute that once again divided the country.

Judah and Benjamin to the south enjoyed the great benefit of having the temple in Jerusalem and the promise that someone from the line of David would always sit on the throne. First Kings records the reign of four kings of Judah, beginning with Rehoboam and ending with Jehosaphat.

Israel in the north, however, was led into idolatry by Jeroboam and never had a good king on the throne. We read about eight of Israel's evil kings in this book. The prophet Elijah communicated God's words to Israel as these wicked kings led the people even further into idolatry. First Kings covers a period of about 120 years.

I Kings
[Kingdom Divided]

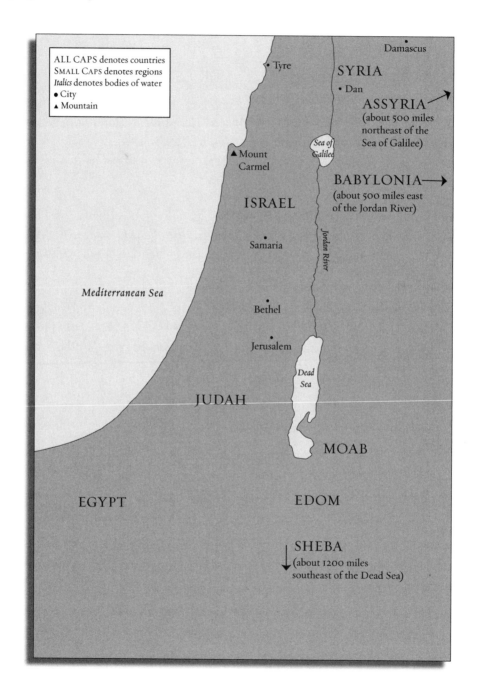

ALL CAPS denotes countries
SMALL CAPS denotes regions
Italics denotes bodies of water
● City
▲ Mountain

• Damascus

• Tyre

SYRIA

• Dan

ASSYRIA →
(about 500 miles
northeast of the
Sea of Galilee)

Sea of Galilee

▲ Mount
Carmel

ISRAEL

BABYLONIA →
(about 500 miles east
of the Jordan River)

•
Samaria

Jordan River

Mediterranean Sea

•
Bethel

•
Jerusalem

Dead Sea

JUDAH

MOAB

EGYPT

EDOM

↓ SHEBA
(about 1200 miles
southeast of the Dead Sea)

I KINGS
[Kingdom Divided]

OVERVIEW

WHO: Author: The prophet Jeremiah (according to Jewish tradition)
Main Characters: Solomon, Rehoboam, Elijah, Jezebel

WHAT: A kingdom divided

WHEN: Covers 120 years (971–851 BC)

WHERE: Israel (united); then divided into Israel to the north and Judah to the south

WHY: A nation divided against itself cannot stand

I.   THE KINGDOM WAS _____ AND THRIVING (1 KINGS 1–11).

    A. King David made a declaration that _____ was to be king and then David died.

    B. Solomon made his most _____ decision just prior to requesting wisdom from God.

       1. He made an alliance with _____.

       2. He _____ one of Pharoah's daughters.

    C. Solomon asked for _____ , and God gave him wisdom, knowledge, and enormous wealth.

    D. The _____ was built and dedicated to the glory of God.

    E. Solomon's _____ reached throughout the ancient world.

    F. Solomon's many foreign _____ turned his heart away from God.

    G. Solomon's heart was a _____ heart.

II.   THE KINGDOM WAS _____ AND DESTROYED (1 KINGS 12–22).

    A. _____ acted unwisely by disregarding the wisdom of his father, Solomon.

B. The once-united kingdom was divided into _____ separate nations.

1. The _____ ten tribes were called Israel.

2. The capital was _____ .

3. The southern two tribes were called _____ .

4. The capital was _____ .

C. _____ was a prophet who God used mightily in warning King Ahab.

APPLICATION

Disobedience brings division in our earthly relationships. But mostly it brings division in the fellowship we as believers enjoy with God. Disobedience begins when we disregard God's Word, and when disobedience makes its start, the inevitable is a divided heart!

I KINGS
[Kingdom Divided]

LEARNING FOR LIFE

1. Review Israel's history from the book of Joshua through the book of 1 Kings (group effort).

2. The Golden Age of Israel began with David but really reached its height during Solomon's reign. What are some of the events and blessings that made that period so extraordinary?

3. What great mistake did Rehoboam make? What principles can we learn from his example?

4. What advantages did Judah have over Israel in its approach to God?

5. What happened when Elijah challenged the priests of Baal at Mount Carmel (1 Kings 18:16-46)? What comfort can we get from this story as we come against huge challenges in our lives today?

I Kings
[Kingdom Divided]

JUST A THOUGHT
The Septuagint may have divided Samuel and Kings into four books because the Greek required more scroll space than the Hebrew.

DAY ONE

COMPLETE READ: Chapters 1–5
QUICK READ: Chapters 1:1–2:12

THE BIG PICTURE

Four full centuries before Israel's kings began one by one to ascend to the throne, God had issued specific instructions and clear warnings about how the kings were to function:

> When you enter the land which the LORD your God gives you, and you possess it and live in it, and you say, "I will set a king over me like all the nations who are around me," you shall surely set a king over you whom the LORD your God chooses, one from among your countrymen you shall set as king over yourselves; you may not put a foreigner over yourselves who is not your countryman. Moreover, he shall not multiply horses for himself, nor shall he cause the people to return to Egypt to multiply horses, since the LORD has said to you, "You shall never again return that way." He shall not multiply wives for himself, or else his heart will turn away; nor shall he greatly increase silver and gold for himself.
>
> DEUTERONOMY 17:14-17

The strength and happiness of a man consists in finding out the way in which God is going, and going that way too.

—HENRY WARD BEECHER, American abolitionist and clergyman

Read 1 Kings 10:1–11:4, a description of Solomon's behavior and some of his accomplishments. Compare these verses to the Deuteronomy verses above. Describe what you find.

NOTE
The books of 1 and 2 Kings have a political rather than religious orientation.

The book of 1 Kings records the sad movement of Israel from a united kingdom to a divided kingdom. Solomon's behavior, which you just read about, laid the groundwork for this devastating civil strife. By the time his reign ended and his son took over the throne, it was just a matter of time — a short time — until division occurred. The following chart shows the major divisions of the book.

David's Last Days		Solomon's Reign		Division of the Kingdom		Elijah's Ministry	
1	2	3	11	12	16	17	22
United Kingdom				Divided Kingdom			
One Nation Becomes Two							

As with 1 and 2 Samuel, 1 and 2 Kings were originally one book, simply titled Kings. Again, the scholars of the Septuagint, the Greek translation of the Old Testament written in the second and third centuries BC, divided this one book into two. They had named the two books of Samuel 1 and 2 Kingdoms. They simply continued this pattern by naming the two books of Kings 3 and 4 Kingdoms.

The author of 1 and 2 Kings is unknown. The Talmud, the rabbinical laws and comments surrounding the laws of Moses, suggests they were written by the prophet Jeremiah. The style, emphasis, and phraseology tend to support this suggestion. If so, they would have been written sometime before 586 BC, the date when Judah was exiled to Babylonia.

Every virtue is a form of obedience to God. Every evil word or act is a form of rebellion against Him.

—STEPHEN NEILL, twentieth-century writer, bishop, and missionary to India

Whoever the author was, he clearly used several historical documents as the sources of material for compiling these books. First Kings 11:41 mentions the book of the acts of Solomon; 1 Kings 14:19 records the existence of the Book of the Chronicles of the Kings of Israel; and 1 Kings 14:29 and 15:7 mention the Book of the Chronicles of the Kings of Judah. Evidently, there was a significant amount of preserved information from which to research and write what we know today as 1 and 2 Kings.

The book of 1 Kings also shows the ministry of the prophet coming into its own as a major force in the life of God's nation, Israel. Our Prominent Player will be Elijah, one of God's bold and courageous spokesmen.

As you read 1 Kings, be aware of how over and over again poor choices brought unwanted and devastating consequences.

Complete today's study by reading again the 1 Kings 2:1-12 portion of your Quick Read. What final insights into David, a man after God's heart, do you see there?

No man is a successful commander who has not first learned to obey.

—Chinese proverb

REVIEW IT!
The theme of 1 Kings is a kingdom divided.

MEMORY VERSE

For when Solomon was old, his wives turned his heart away after other gods.

1 KINGS 11:4

I KINGS
[Kingdom Divided]

FACT
The period of Hebrew history during David and Solomon's reigns is considered the Golden Era.

DAY TWO

COMPLETE READ: Chapters 6–10
QUICK READ: Chapter 12

A CRUCIAL CHAPTER

Billie Burke, the once-famous actress, was traveling across the Atlantic when she noticed a gentleman at the next table suffering with a miserable cold. "Are you uncomfortable?" she asked. The man nodded. "I'll tell you just what to do for it," she said. "Go back to your stateroom and drink lots of orange juice. Take two aspirins. Cover yourself with all the blankets you can find. Sweat the cold out. I know just what I'm talking about. I'm Billie Burke from Hollywood." The man smiled warmly. "Thanks," he said. "I'm Dr. Mayo of the Mayo Clinic."[1]

Receiving advice is tricky. First, you had better know who is giving the advice, and second, you had better know your relationship to that person. Rehoboam, in 1 Kings 12, missed it on both counts. The eventual result was the division of Israel into two nations.

Read 1 Kings 12:1-14 and describe the events recorded there. What is your reaction to Rehoboam's behavior and decision in light of the suggestions for receiving advice given in the previous paragraph?

If you ask enough people, you can usually find someone who will advise you to do what you were going to do anyway.
—WESTON SMITH

A "high place"
(1 Kings 12:31) was a
geographically elevated
place with an altar and
a tree or pole of wood
as an idol.

Because of Rehoboam's actions in 931 BC, Jeroboam and ten of the tribes rebelled against him. Only the tribes of Judah and Benjamin in the southern part of the country remained loyal to Rehoboam. This division lasted until both nations eventually went into captivity because of their rebellion against God — the northern kingdom of Israel in 722 BC and the southern kingdom of Judah in 586 BC.

Immediately following the division, Jeroboam began to establish the North as a permanent separate nation. He set up a capital city in Shechem (12:25) to match the capital of Jerusalem in the South. But he went even further than that. Read 12:26-33. List and explain all the counterfeits he manufactured to keep the people loyal to him.

Every one of us is, even from his mother's womb, a master craftsman of idols.

—John Calvin, founder of Calvinism

This was the beginning of the end for the nation of Israel in the North. Jeroboam made false gods for the people to worship, false priests for the people to follow, and false feast days for the people to celebrate. Subsequent kings followed in his steps and slid even deeper into idolatry. Time and again we read words like those in 1 Kings 16:25-26: "Omri did evil in the sight of the LORD, and acted more wickedly than all who were before him. For he walked in all the way of Jeroboam the son of Nebat and in his sins which he made Israel sin, provoking the LORD God of Israel with their idols."

Idolatry was the sin for which God had to discipline them. He sent the prophets Hosea and Amos to call them back to Himself, but the people refused to listen and repent. They had grabbed on to idolatry and in return, idolatry grabbed on to them. And they could not free themselves.

Remember what an idol is: anything that usurps the attention, honor, and allegiance due to God. Looking back over this study, is there any response you need to make to God?

You don't have to go to heathen lands today to find false gods. America is full of them. Whatever you love more than God is your idol.

—D. L. MOODY, American evangelist of the nineteenth century

MEMORY VERSE

For when Solomon was old, his wives turned his heart away after other gods.

1 KINGS 11:4

REVIEW IT! Chapter 12 is a Crucial Chapter because it describes the division of Israel into two nations.

I KINGS
[Kingdom Divided]

DAY THREE

COMPLETE READ: Chapters 11–14
QUICK READ: Chapter 18

A PROMINENT PLAYER

Those who take a stand. Those who hold their ground. Those who don't cave under pressure. We hold these people in awe. Jesus in the garden. Martin Luther before the council. Martyrs facing the lions.

And don't forget Elijah—that rugged man who prophesied for God to the people of the northern kingdom of Israel at a time when they had no use for him or his message. He had his moments of failure, but when the whole of his life is considered, it is easy to see that he stood for God and often felt that he stood alone.

He carried out his prophetic ministry during the times of ungodly King Ahab and his more ungodly Queen Jezebel. They had taken the sins of Jeroboam, son of Nebat, and made them look like Sunday school children's pranks. They had taken idolatry to its lowest levels by introducing the worship of Baal (the god of Jezebel) and the worship of the Asherah (wooden symbols of a female deity). Finally, the tension between Elijah and Ahab reached the point where confrontation was inevitable.

Read 1 Kings 18:16-24 and describe the confrontation as it was set up.

Perfect courage is to do unwitnessed what we should be capable of doing before all the world.

—DUC DE LA ROCHEFOUCAULD, seventeenth-century French author and moralist

Read 18:25-29. As this scene progressed, what do you think Baal's followers were thinking and feeling? How about Ahab?

NOTE
Elijah's name is mentioned twenty-nine times in the New Testament.

Finish the story by reading 18:30-40. Again, summarize what happened in your own words.

As you look back over this story, what traits do you see in Elijah that enabled him to perform one of the boldest feats of faith in history?

Courage is not the absence of fear, but the judgment that something else is more important than fear.

—AMBROSE REDMOON, twentieth-century writer

In the next chapter, Elijah began to crack from extreme pressure and exhaustion. Yet the angel of the Lord ministered to him, and he rebounded with great fervor and continued a strong prophetic ministry of standing up for God in the midst of incredible evil. Then one day, "As they [Elijah and his chosen heir, Elisha] were going along and talking, behold, there appeared a chariot of fire and horses of fire which separated the two of them. And Elijah went up by a whirlwind to heaven" (2 Kings 2:11). A grand promotion for a great prophet!

Most of us will never be called to stand toe to toe with four hundred prophets of Baal and do spiritual battle. But in one way or another, day after day, we are called on to take a stand.

What does taking a stand, holding your ground, and not caving under pressure mean to you in your walk with God?

Write down any helpful insights you have gained from reading about Elijah and his stand that day on Mount Carmel.

REVIEW IT!
Elijah is our Prominent Player because he took a stand against wicked King Ahab and the prophets of Baal.

Memory Verse

For when Solomon was old, his wives turned his heart away after other gods.

1 Kings 11:4

I KINGS
[Kingdom Divided]

DAY FOUR

COMPLETE READ: Chapters 15–18
QUICK READ: Chapter 8

A NOTABLE FEATURE

Whether we like it or not, asking is the rule of the Kingdom.
—C. H. SPURGEON

In his excellent book titled *Prayer: Finding the Heart's True Home*, Richard J. Foster explores numerous dimensions of prayer. In his discussion of petitionary prayer, he takes to task the belief that asking God for things is a lesser, cruder form of prayer than merely adoring God's attributes without asking for anything. He writes, "Petitionary Prayer remains primary throughout our lives because we are forever dependent on God. It is something that we never really 'get beyond,' nor should we even want to. In fact, the Hebrew and Greek words that are generally used for prayer mean 'to request' or 'to make a petition.'"[3]

Foster goes on to say that not only is the Bible full of petitionary prayers, but the Bible itself instructs us to pray this way. When the disciples asked Jesus to teach them to pray, He gave them what we call the Lord's Prayer — a prayer primarily of petition.

A Notable Feature of the book of I Kings is an extended prayer of petition in chapter 8. Solomon had just completed the construction and furnishing of the temple. We read in 8:22, "Then Solomon stood before the altar of the LORD in the presence of all the assembly of Israel and spread out his hands toward heaven." His prayer of dedication, to be sure, began with adoration, praise, and thanksgiving. But very quickly it turned to an

INTERESTING!
Because of its advanced refinery system, Solomon's city of Ezion-Geber has been called "the Pittsburgh of Palestine."[2]

Heaven is full of answers to prayers for which no one ever bothered to ask.
—BILLY GRAHAM, American evangelist and preacher

extended outpouring of petition after petition to the God of Israel. We will concentrate on verses 22-53, part of your Quick Read for today. As you investigate these verses, respond to the following questions or statements.

List all of Solomon's petitions and include a brief explanation of each one.

What do you think Solomon's thoughts, attitudes, intentions, and motivations were as he prayed this extraordinary prayer of petition?

Just as in earthly life lovers long for the moment when they are able to breathe forth their love for each other, to let their souls blend in a soft whisper, so the mystic longs for the moment when in prayer he can, as it were, creep into God.

—SØREN KIERKEGAARD, Danish philosopher and Christian theologian

What picture of God does Solomon present throughout this prayer?

What have you learned about prayers of petition from this study that will enrich your own prayer life?

In closing his chapter on petitionary prayer, Foster quotes Herbert Farmer: "If prayer is the heart of religion, then petition is the heart of prayer."[5]

What petition do you need to take to God right now?

MEMORY VERSE

For when Solomon was old, his wives turned his heart away after other gods.

1 KINGS 11:4

REVIEW IT!
Chapter 8 is a Notable Feature as an excellent example of petitionary prayer.

I KINGS
[Kingdom Divided]

DID YOU KNOW?
Solomon wrote Psalm 72.

DAY FIVE

COMPLETE READ: Chapters 19–22
QUICK READ: Chapter 11

A TIMELESS PRINCIPLE

A garden can be a very rewarding experience. After the work and sweat of cultivating, planting, fertilizing, and tending comes the beauty of the fruits. Vivian Glyck writes in her book *12 Lessons on Life I Learned from My Garden,*

> The dog days of summer are pure bliss in my garden. No matter how lousy a gardener I have been that season, there comes a point when everything seems to bloom. I wade into the lushness of tomato plants that tickle my waist, step gingerly over the massive cucumber leaves that have grown big enough to protect their fruit from the harsh summer rays, and stoop to inspect the many varieties of peppers that are growing vigorously.[6]

Experience teaches that love of flowers and vegetables is not enough to make a man a good gardener. He must also hate weeds.

—BURTON HILLIS

But no matter how nice a garden is looking, inevitably you have to leave it for a time — maybe just a week or two for a family emergency or vacation. And when you get back, your garden has already taken on the look of a neglected orphan. Predators have crept in, weeds have taken over, and the work required to return your garden to its pristine condition seems daunting.

The garden is a helpful metaphor for the heart. It too must be cultivated, planted, fertilized, and tended before the richness of spiritual fruit begins to appear. And, ignore your heart for just a short time and predators creep in and weeds sprout faster than you can imagine.

Our Timeless Principle for the book of 1 Samuel also encouraged us to think about our hearts. There we quoted Proverbs 4:23, which says, "Watch over your heart with all diligence, for from it flow the springs of life." What grows in our hearts spills out in our lives.

At the end of Solomon's beautiful prayer of petition in 1 Kings, he added a few closing comments to the people—a postscript to the occasion. Read 1 Kings 8:54-61 and describe what he said about their hearts, particularly in verses 58 and 61.

JUST A THOUGHT
Solomon wrote the book of Ecclesiastes, which is a prolonged description of a wandering heart.

Verses 62-66 describe the response of Solomon and the people to God following Solomon's extensive prayers and postscript. Explain what they did and what you sense the condition of their hearts was at this time in relation to their walk with God.

Now move ahead to 1 Kings 11, your Quick Read for today. As you read verses 1-8, remember the words of Solomon in 1 Kings 8:58 and 61 about the heart. Describe his heart condition and the cause of it in 11:1-8 and compare it to what you read in 8:58,61.

See that your chief study be about your heart, that there God's image may be planted.
—RICHARD BAXTER,
seventeenth-century
English Puritan author

Somewhere along the journey Solomon neglected his heart, and predators and weeds invaded. And his heart turned from God to gods. Take a moment to think about actual or potential predators and weeds that threaten the health of your heart. We all have them. What are yours? Sometimes writing them down makes them clearer and easier to address.

How should you, together with God, deal with these issues?

MEMORY VERSE

For when Solomon was old, his wives turned his heart away after other gods.

1 KINGS 11:4

I KINGS
[Kingdom Divided]

REVIEW

1. The theme of 1 Kings is a _____ divided.

2. Chapter 12 is a Crucial Chapter because it describes the _____ of Israel into two nations.

3. _____ is our Prominent Player because he took a stand against wicked King Ahab and the prophets of Baal.

4. Chapter 8 is a Notable Feature as an excellent example of _____ prayer.

5. "For when _____ was old, his wives turned his heart away after other gods."

1 KINGS 11:_____

2 KINGS

[Kingdoms Exiled]

They rejected His statutes and His covenant which

He made with their fathers and His warnings

with which He warned them.

2 KINGS 17:15

SEVEN

2 KINGS
[Kingdoms Exiled]

INTRODUCTION

Second Kings covers the reigns of eleven wicked kings in Israel until its captivity by Assyria in 722 BC and the reigns of sixteen kings in Judah until it was exiled to Babylon in 586 BC. The prophet Elisha took over the job of speaking for God in Israel when Elijah was taken up to heaven. God continued to work mightily on behalf of His people, but in the end, their idolatry and wickedness brought about discipline and judgment.

By the end of The Kingdom Books, Israel was scattered, Jerusalem and the temple were destroyed, and Judah had been taken into exile in Babylon. The great dream, the hope for a nation that would be a blessing to all the nations, had been shattered as rebellious Israel and Judah refused to obey and worship the only true God.

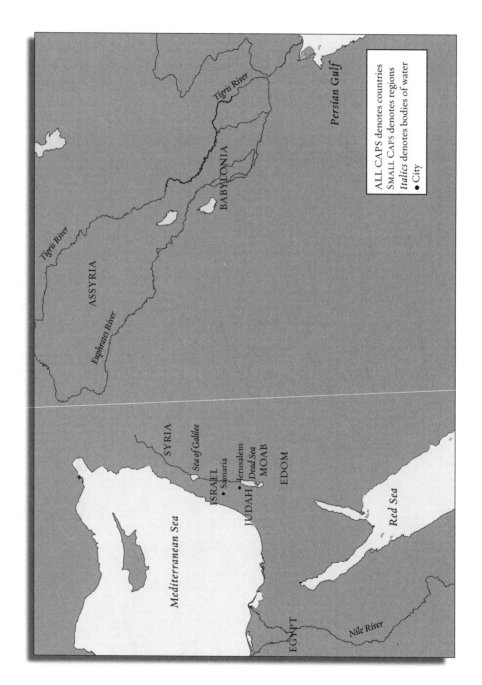

ALL CAPS denotes countries
SMALL CAPS denotes regions
Italics denotes bodies of water
● City

Tigris River

Tigris River

Euphrates River

ASSYRIA

BABYLONIA

Persian Gulf

SYRIA

Sea of Galilee

ISRAEL
● Samaria

JUDAH
● Jerusalem

Dead Sea

MOAB

EDOM

Mediterranean Sea

EGYPT

Nile River

Red Sea

2 KINGS
[Kingdoms Exiled]

OVERVIEW

WHO: Author: Possibly Jeremiah or the "sons of the prophets"
Main Characters: Elijah, Elisha, the kings of Israel, the kings of Judah

WHAT: Decline and captivity of the two kingdoms

WHEN: Israel: 853–722 BC; Judah: 853–586 BC; Babylonia: 585–560 BC

WHERE: Israel, the northern kingdom, whose capital was Samaria; Judah, the southern kingdom, whose capital was Jerusalem; Babylonia

WHY: The kings led the people away from God and into exile

I. GOD'S WARNINGS WERE GIVEN THROUGH ELIJAH AND _____ .

   A. After Elijah ascended into heaven in a chariot of fire, _____ succeeded him.

   B. Elisha's ministry to Israel was very _____ from his mentor, Elijah.

   C. Elisha's ministry lasted _____ years from King Jehoram to King Jehoash.

   D. God will eventually judge and _____ His people.

II. THE KINGS OF ISRAEL _____ GOD'S WARNINGS.

   A. All the kings of the northern kingdom were _____ .

   B. The northern kingdom lasted _____ years.

   C. Israel had _____ kings.

   D. God _____ Israel from His sight.

   E. In 722 BC, the Assyrians conquered Israel and _____ the ten tribes.

III. THE KINGS OF _____ IGNORED GOD'S WARNINGS.

A. Judah had _____ kings.

B. Only _____ kings did what was right.

C. God removed _____ from His presence.

D. The _____ conquered the southern tribes in 586 BC.

E. The people were taken to Babylon in _____ for seventy years.

APPLICATION

As the leader goes, so go the people. Who are you leading? Where are you taking them?

2 KINGS
[Kingdoms Exiled]

LEARNING FOR LIFE

1. Review the history of Israel from the book of Joshua to the book of 2 Kings (group effort).

2. What role did Elisha have in the history of Israel?

3. How, why, and through what country did God punish Israel?

4. How, why, and through what country did God punish Judah?

5. What lesson did you learn from the video on 2 Kings, and how can that lesson be applied to your life?

2 KINGS
[Kingdoms Exiled]

DID YOU KNOW?
The "sons of the prophets" (2 Kings 2:3) were probably young men who studied the law and history of Israel in preparation for teaching the people.

DAY ONE

COMPLETE READ: Chapters 1–5
QUICK READ: Chapters 1–2

THE BIG PICTURE

Jeremiah was a prophet to the nation of Judah during its last days of decline just before its captivity. Several times in his messages to the people, he captured the essence of their hearts as he spoke God's words to them:

> Yet they did not listen to Me or incline their ear, but stiffened their neck; they did more evil than their fathers.
>
> JEREMIAH 7:26

> Yet they did not listen or incline their ears, but stiffened their necks in order not to listen or take correction.
>
> JEREMIAH 17:23

Bow stubborn knees!
—WILLIAM SHAKESPEARE,
sixteenth-century English dramatist and poet

> Behold, I am about to bring on this city and all its towns the entire calamity that I have declared against it, because they have stiffened their necks so as not to heed My words.
>
> JEREMIAH 19:15

The author of Proverbs 29:1 states, "A man who hardens his neck after much reproof will suddenly be broken beyond remedy." In the book of 2 Kings, both nations, Israel and Judah, continually stiffened their necks against God's powerful words of rebuke and His tender words imploring repentance. Occasionally they responded, but it was always short-lived. A downhill trajectory ended with captivity by foreign nations. The chart that follows shows the broad divisions of this story.

Continued Decline of Israel and Judah	Capivity of Israel by Assyria	Continued Decline of Judah	Capivity of Judah by Babylonia
1 12	13 17	18 23	24 25
Divided Kingdom		Surviving Kingdom	
Two Nations Become None			

Second Kings intersperses the stories of the two nations. We follow a number of years of Israel's history, and then we are brought up to date on Judah's history. We return to Israel, then to Judah again, and so on. Once Israel's captivity by Assyria in 722 BC is recorded in chapter 17, the remainder of the book chronicles Judah's final decline and eventual captivity by Babylonia in 586 BC.

Day One in your study of 1 Kings included information about the title and author of 2 Kings. Here are some chronological facts to help you put the timeline of 2 Kings in perspective:

- Nation of Israel: lasted 209 years (931–722 BC)

- Nation of Judah: lasted 345 years (931–586 BC)

- 2 Kings 1–17: covers 131 years (853–722 BC)

- 2 Kings 18–25: covers 155 years (715–560 BC)

The book of 2 Kings spans 293 years (853–560 BC) — 293 years of idolatry, immorality, and disunity punctuated only briefly by periods of true worship, morality, and unity.

Although 2 Kings is a continuation and completion of the story begun in 1 Kings, it is helpful to compare and contrast the two books, as the following chart does.

Repentance may be old-fashioned, but it is not outdated so long as there is sin.
—J. C. Macaulay, preacher and author

1 KINGS	2 KINGS
Opens with David, king of Israel	Closes with Nebuchadnezzar, king of Babylonia
Solomon's glory	Jehoiachin's shame
The temple built and consecrated	The temple violated and destroyed
Begins with blessings for obedience	Ends with judgment for disobedience
The growth of apostasy	The consequences of apostasy
The united kingdom is divided	The two kingdoms are destroyed

As you read 2 Kings, ask God to sensitize you to the danger of a stiffened response to His prodding, prompting, and pleading in your life.

True repentance has a double aspect. It looks upon things past with a weeping eye, and upon the future with a watchful eye.

—ROBERT SOUTH, English preacher of the seventeenth century

REVIEW IT!
The theme of 2 Kings is decline and captivity of the two kingdoms.

MEMORY VERSE

They rejected His statutes and His covenant which He made with their fathers and His warnings with which He warned them.

2 KINGS 17:15

2 KINGS
[Kingdoms Exiled]

DAY TWO

COMPLETE READ: Chapters 6–10
QUICK READ: Chapters 18–19

PROMINENT PLAYER NUMBER 1

Because the kings are the leading characters in the book of 2 Kings, we will study two of them this week, omitting the Crucial Chapter and adding an additional Prominent Player.

One of the basic maxims of leadership is that a leader defines reality. Warren Bennis and Burt Nanus in their book *Leaders* give a prime example of this:

> This reliance on "someone" to define reality in a group is well illustrated by a favorite anecdote, a baseball story. It takes place in the last inning of a very key game, playoff for the pennant, ninth inning, with 3-2 on the batter. The final pitch comes over, the umpire hesitates a split second. The batter angrily turns around and says, "Well, what was it?" The umpire then replies, "It ain't nothin' 'til I call it."[1]

Hezekiah, the thirteenth king of the southern nation of Judah, was one of the few kings of either nation of whom it is written: "He did right in the sight of the LORD" (2 Kings 18:3). Crucial to his doing right was his ability to carry out that basic maxim of a leader — to define reality. And when he defined it, he got it right.

He was only twenty-five years old when he took over the throne of Judah (2 Kings 18:2), but he had a great ability to see what needed to be done and immediately set about doing it. Interestingly, the

The man who wants to lead the orchestra must turn his back on the crowd.

—JAMES CROOK, writer

only modeling he could have received from his father, Ahaz, was negative, as it is recorded of Ahaz: "He did not do what was right in the sight of the LORD his God" (2 Kings 16:2).

Read 2 Kings 18:1-8 and list the accomplishments of Hezekiah that are described there.

DID YOU KNOW?
Part of Hezekiah's story is also told in Isaiah 36–39.

Based on what he did, describe in your own words how Hezekiah must have defined reality when he became king and analyzed the existing situation.

Read 2 Kings 18:13-27 to get a sense of what was taking place at that time. Then read 19:1-7 and again describe how Hezekiah must have defined reality based on the action he took.

Reality is usually something you could not have guessed.
—C. S. LEWIS, English essayist, novelist, and Christian apologist

Beginning in 19:8, Hezekiah faced another situation requiring an honest appraisal and a clear definition of reality. Obviously, his definition determined the action he took. As you read 19:8-20,32-37, describe his definition of reality, the action he took, and what resulted.

Time after time, Hezekiah was able to read the situation, decide what needed to be done or whom he needed to turn to for help, and then do it — promptly. As you live your life, how well do you perceive reality, define it, and then respond accordingly? Is there some new level of insight, discernment, or courage that you need to ask God to develop in you so you are better able to do this?

MEMORY VERSE

They rejected His statutes and His covenant which He made with their fathers and His warnings with which He warned them.

2 KINGS 17:15

REVIEW IT!
Hezekiah is a Prominent Player because he was able to define reality and respond accordingly.

DAY THREE

COMPLETE READ: Chapters 11–15
QUICK READ: Chapter 21

PROMINENT PLAYER NUMBER 2

Jonathan Edwards, born in 1703, was one of America's greatest theologians, pastors, writers, and scholars. He and his wife had eleven children. Of his known male descendants:

- More than 300 became pastors, missionaries, or theological professors

- 120 were professors at various universities

- 110 became attorneys

- 60 were prominent authors

- 30 were judges

- 14 served as presidents of universities and colleges

- 3 served in the U.S. Congress

- 1 became vice-president of the United States[2]

This is the very worst wickedness, that we refuse to acknowledge the passionate evil that is in us. This makes us secret and rotten.

—D. H. LAWRENCE, English novelist

If you know anything about Edwards' life, you might be tempted to say, "Well, that makes sense. Such a godly man is bound to produce such a godly posterity." But for some reason — and only God knows why — that doesn't always happen. This is exactly the case with our Prominent Player Number 2, Manasseh. His father, whose life we studied in Day Two, "did right in the sight of the LORD" (2 Kings 18:3). But Manasseh "did evil in the sight of the LORD, according to the abominations of the nations whom the LORD dispossessed before the sons of Israel" (2 Kings 21:2).

Second Kings 21:1-9 is a catalog of the abominations that Manasseh, king of Judah, committed. List these abominations and, when helpful, describe the abomination. Note: A good Bible dictionary can help you with terms and phrases such as "Baal," "Asherah," and "made his son pass through the fire" (child sacrifice).

IRONIC
Manasseh, the most wicked king of Judah, reigned the longest of any king— fifty-five years.

What thoughts and feelings did you have as you worked through these verses?

What insights into human nature did you have as you studied this material?

God responded to the wickedness of Manasseh in a very strong way. Second Kings 21:10-15 describes in a number of ways what God would do and what the result would be. Clearly explain these in writing.

Most people repent their sins by thanking God they ain't so wicked as their neighbors.

—Josh Billings, American aphorist and humorist of the nineteenth century

What thoughts and feelings did you have as you worked through these verses?

What insights into God's character did you have as you studied this material?

Studying abominations like these committed by the son of a godly man can be sobering. How has this study affected you?

MEMORY VERSE

They rejected His statutes and His covenant which He made with their fathers and His warnings with which He warned them.

2 KINGS 17:15

2 KINGS
[Kingdoms Exiled]

DAY FOUR

COMPLETE READ: Chapters 16–20

QUICK READ: Chapters 17:1-18; 24–25

A NOTABLE FEATURE

In AD 49, the apostle Paul wrote, "Do not be deceived, God is not mocked; for whatever a man sows, this he will also reap" (Galatians 6:7).

In 722 BC (771 years before Paul wrote these words), the northern kingdom of Israel experienced the truth of them. They sowed idolatry and they reaped captivity by Assyria, the world power at that time.

In 586 BC (636 years before Paul wrote these words), the southern kingdom of Judah experienced the truth of them. They sowed idolatry and they reaped captivity by Babylonia, the world power at that time.

Assyria's foreign policy was to scatter their conquered peoples into different parts of the world, thus keeping them from coalescing into a rebellious force. So it was that the ten tribes of Israel were scattered in varying locations across the Near East.

Babylonia's foreign policy was to resettle their conquered people in Babylonia, thus keeping them close by to more easily maintain control. Therefore, the two tribes of Judah took up residence in Babylonia.

Second Kings 17:1-6 briefly describes the actual siege and captivity of Israel. Verses 7-18 go on to describe what the Israelites had sown and what they reaped.

Summarize these sins in a way that is meaningful to you.

What does verse 13 tell you about the heart of God?

Chapters 24 and 25 describe the captivity of Judah by Babylonia. The Exile of Judah to Babylonia occurred in three stages:

605 BC	597 BC	586 BC
King Jehoiakim	King Jehoiachin	King Zedekiah
2 Kings 24:1-7	2 Kings 24:8-16	2 Kings 24:17–25:21

Sowing is not as difficult as reaping.
—JOHANN WOLFGANG VON GOETHE, German poet

In contrast to the description of Israel's captivity in 2 Kings 17, which focuses on the sins committed by Israel, the description of Judah's captivity focuses on the destruction perpetrated by Babylonia. As you read 2 Kings 24:1–25:21, summarize that destruction as it applies to the following people and places.

The people:

The city:

The temple:

The king:

These two captivities are sad moments in biblical history. In them, we see God needing to discipline His own people in severe ways. But He had warned them time and time again for centuries. And in the end, they reaped what they sowed. Following the discipline, God brought them back to Himself — He did not give up on them or write them off. After judgment, there was hope. In fact, never again would Israel worship idols. But at this point in the story, there was only sadness.

In your personal life, have you had any experiences with the sowing and reaping principle? Feel free to describe your experiences if you are comfortable doing so.

DID YOU KNOW?
During this time,
Glaucus of Chios
invented soldering
of iron.

I clearly recognize that all good is in God alone, and that in me, without Divine Grace, there is nothing but deficiency. . . . The one sole thing in myself in which I glory is that I see in myself nothing in which I can glory.

—CATHERINE OF GENOA, fifteenth-century Italian mystic and saint

Meditate on the grace of God that brought you back to Him. Then thank Him for His grace—always present, even in the midst of discipline.

> For those whom the Lord loves He disciplines.... It is for discipline that you endure; God deals with you as with sons; for what son is there whom his father does not discipline?... They disciplined us for a short time as seemed best to them, but He disciplines us for our good, so that we may share His holiness. All discipline for the moment seems not to be joyful, but sorrowful; yet to those who have been trained by it, afterwards it yields the peaceful fruit of righteousness.
>
> HEBREWS 12:6-7,10-11

Oh! for a spirit that bows always before the sovereignty of God!
—CHARLES SPURGEON, nineteenth-century British preacher

REVIEW IT!
Our Notable Feature is the two captivities and how they vividly picture the sowing and reaping principle.

MEMORY VERSE

They rejected His statutes and His covenant which He made with their fathers and His warnings with which He warned them.

2 KINGS 17:15

2 KINGS
[Kingdoms Exiled]

DAY FIVE

COMPLETE READ: Chapters 21–25
QUICK READ: Chapters 22–23

LEGACY
Josiah followed in the
godly steps of his great-
grandfather Hezekiah.

A TIMELESS PRINCIPLE

John Chrysostom, a fourth-century church father, emphasized the importance of consistent contact with the Word of God:

> Your wife provokes you, for example, your son grieves you, your servant angers you, your enemy plots against you, your friend envies you, your neighbor curses you, your fellow soldier trips you up, often a law suit threatens you, poverty troubles you, loss of your property gives you grief, prosperity puffs you up, misfortune depresses you, and many causes and compulsions to discouragement and grief, to conceit and desperation surround us on all sides, and a multitude of missiles falls from everywhere. Therefore we have a continuous need for the full armor of the Scriptures. . . . We must thoroughly quench the darts of the devil and beat them off by continual reading of the divine Scriptures. For it is not possible, not possible for anyone to be saved without continually taking advantage of spiritual reading.[3]

Over and over again, God Himself also stresses the importance of the Scriptures to us. Consider these three passages:

> "You shall meditate on it day and night."
>
> JOSHUA 1:8

He helped me understand that it is a daily meditation on scripture in which one reads not for knowledge or information but to enhance one's life of faith.

—KATHLEEN NORRIS, poet and author

They are more desirable than gold, yes, than
much fine gold.

PSALM 19:10

All Scripture is inspired by God and profitable
for teaching, for reproof, for correction, for
training in righteousness.

2 TIMOTHY 3:16

God's desires for the kings of His people were no different. On
Day One of our 1 Kings study, we looked at Deuteronomy 17
and saw instructions given by God for the kings four hundred
years before an earthly king ruled His people. But there is more
in this great passage. Read Deuteronomy 17:18-20 and write
down what the king was supposed to do regarding the law of
God and why he was supposed to do it.

*One gem from that
ocean is worth all the
pebbles from earthly
streams.*

—ROBERT M'CHEYNE,
nineteenth-century
Scottish pastor and
evangelist

Now look at your Quick Read for today. Summarize in your
own words what takes place in chapter 22. What does this tell
you about the kings' response to Deuteronomy 17:18-20 over
the years?

Chapter 23 chronicles Josiah's response to his reading of the Scriptures that were found. Summarize in a way that is helpful to you everything he did in response to what he read.

DID YOU KNOW?
During this time, the Greek poets Tyrtaetus and Mimnermus wrote elegies and songs of love and war.

Our actions often make our attitudes visible. How would you describe Josiah's attitude throughout this process?

Hebrews 4:12 says, "For the word of God is living and active and sharper than any two-edged sword, and piercing as far as the division of soul and spirit, of both joints and marrow, and able to judge the thoughts and intentions of the heart."

The Word of God obviously had this effect on Josiah and most likely on many of the people around him. Can you describe a time in your life when the Scriptures impacted you in such a way that you responded without delay? Record the details of that experience.

Through His words we come to know God Himself, His exact will, His way of looking at things, His most intimate desires, His holy countenance.
—CARLO CARETTO, twentieth-century Catholic spiritual writer

For the Word of God to have that kind of power in our lives, we must practice, in John Chrysostom's words, a "continual reading of the divine Scriptures." As you evaluate your habits of personal contact with the Bible, do you see any adjustments that need to be made? If so, what are they, and how can you begin to make them?

What would happen to us if we would more deeply believe the truth — God speaks! God speaks to me! This is the heart of prayer — that God is speaking directly to me in Scripture.

—EDWARD J. FARRELL, author and spiritual director

MEMORY VERSE

They rejected His statutes and His covenant which He made with their fathers and His warnings with which He warned them.

2 KINGS 17:15

2 KINGS
[Kingdoms Exiled]

REVIEW

1. The theme of 2 Kings is decline and _____ of the two kingdoms.

2. _____ is a Prominent Player because he was able to define reality and respond accordingly.

3. _____ is Prominent Player Number 2 because he committed abominations worse than any other king of Judah.

4. Our Notable Feature is the two _____ and how they vividly picture the sowing and reaping principle.

5. "They rejected His statutes and His _____ which He made with their fathers and His warnings with which He warned them."

2 KINGS 17:_____

Comprehensive Review of
THE KINGDOM BOOKS

JOSHUA

1. The theme of Joshua is conquering and settling the _____ Land.

2. Our Crucial Chapter is chapter 1 because it portrays Joshua's transition into _____ leadership position.

3. A Prominent Player in the book is _____ , who displays a strong, godly character.

4. A Notable Feature of Joshua is the contribution of the elderly _____ .

5. "So the LORD gave Israel all the _____ which He had sworn to give to their fathers, and they possessed it and lived in it."

JOSHUA 21:_____

JUDGES

1. The theme of Judges is everyone did as he _____.

2. Our Crucial Chapter is chapter 1 because it describes the failure to drive out the _____ of the land.

3. The occurrence of seven _____, each with the same events, is the Notable Feature of Judges.

4. The _____ are the Prominent Players in the book of Judges, carrying a wide range of responsibilities.

5. "In those days there was no _____ in Israel; everyone did what was right in his own eyes."

JUDGES 21:_____

RUTH

1. The theme of Ruth is living out the law of the kinsman _____.

2. Chapter _____ is the Crucial Chapter because it prepares us for the kinsman redeemer episode.

3. Our Prominent Player is _____ because of her struggle with bitterness in the light of life's difficulties.

4. The Notable Feature of the book of Ruth is the _____ redeemer concept.

5. "Blessed is the LORD who has not left you without a _____ today."

RUTH 4:_____

I SAMUEL

1. The theme of I Samuel is "Give us a _____!"—Israel becomes a monarchy.

2. Chapter 8 is the Crucial Chapter because it is the bridge that moves Israel from a theocracy to a _____.

3. _____ is a Prominent Player because he had all the makings of a great king.

4. Saul is a Prominent Player because his _____ overcame his strengths and caused him to sin and lose his kingship.

5. "Man looks at the outward appearance, but the LORD looks at the _____."

I SAMUEL 16:_____

2 Samuel

1. The theme of 2 Samuel is David establishes the _____.

2. Chapter 7 is our Crucial Chapter because in it, God institutes the _____ covenant.

3. Our Prominent Player is _____, a man after God's heart.

4. Chapter 22 is a Notable Feature because it pictures the awesomeness of _____ in the midst of our trials.

5. "May the house of Your servant _____ be established before You."

2 Samuel 7:_____

1 Kings

1. The theme of 1 Kings is a _____ divided.

2. Chapter 12 is a Crucial Chapter because it describes the _____ of Israel into two nations.

3. _____ is our Prominent Player because he took a stand against wicked King Ahab and the prophets of Baal.

4. Chapter 8 is a Notable Feature as an excellent example of _____ prayer.

5. "For when _____ was old, his wives turned his heart away after other gods."

1 Kings 11:_____

2 Kings

1. The theme of 2 Kings is decline and _____ of the two kingdoms.

2. _____ is a Prominent Player because he was able to define reality and respond accordingly.

3. _____ is Prominent Player Number 2 because he committed abominations worse than any other king of Judah.

4. Our Notable Feature is the two _____ and how they vividly picture the sowing and reaping principle.

5. "They rejected His statutes and His _____ which He made with their fathers and His warnings with which He warned them."

2 Kings 17:_____

CONGRATULATIONS!

You have just completed The Kingdom Books, and it is our prayer (Yes, we really are praying for you!) that you have learned for life what the first twelve books of the Bible are all about.

In The Pentateuch and The Kingdom Books, we have traveled from the Garden of Eden to Canaan, on to Egypt and then to Mount Sinai, through the wilderness, and back to Canaan. We have seen the children of Israel rely on God and conquer the land He had given them. We have watched as they turned from their holy God and embraced false gods and perverted ways of worship. They have been conquered, and they have been delivered by God's grace. The nation has split in two, and kings after kings have ruled. All the rulers in Israel have been evil, but Judah has seen several good kings and enjoyed times of great spiritual revival. But at the close of 2 Kings, all has been destroyed, including the two nations, Jerusalem, and most importantly, the temple of the living God. All is lost, and all seems hopeless.

But above all else, God is a God of hope! Now that you have completed set two of *The Amazing Collection*, we hope you have come to see the majesty, power, love, and faithfulness of God but have not missed the fact that God is also a judge and will discipline His children. He will not, however, leave His children without hope.

As you begin set three, The Post-Exilic Books, you will see again that God has not forgotten His children nor has He forgotten His promises. He will bring them back to Jerusalem and help them rebuild the temple and restore the people to worship.

Stand back! The journey through the Bible continues with The Post-Exilic Books! It is an amazing journey! It is an Amazing Collection!

Chronological Relationship of the Old Testament Books

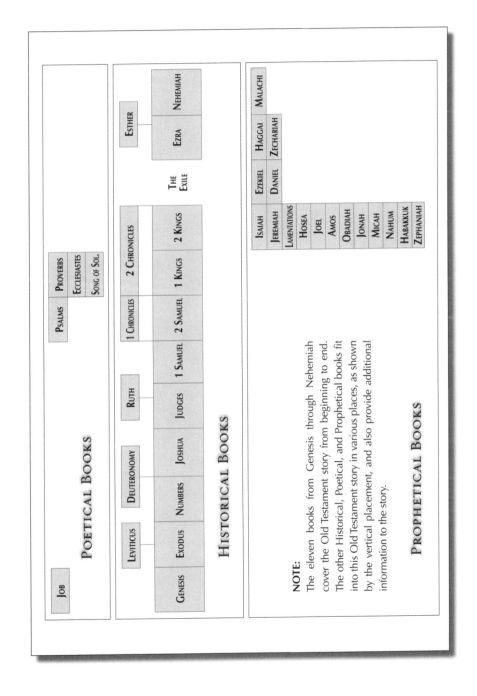

Poetical Books

Job

Psalms | Proverbs
Ecclesiastes
Song of Sol.

Historical Books

Genesis | Exodus | Numbers | Deuteronomy | Joshua | Judges | Ruth | 1 Samuel | 2 Samuel | 1 Chronicles | 1 Kings | 2 Chronicles | 2 Kings

Leviticus

The Exile

Esther

Ezra | Nehemiah

Prophetical Books

Isaiah | Ezekiel | Haggai | Malachi
Jeremiah | Daniel | Zechariah
Lamentations
Hosea
Joel
Amos
Obadiah
Jonah
Micah
Nahum
Habakkuk
Zephaniah

NOTE:
The eleven books from Genesis through Nehemiah cover the Old Testament story from beginning to end. The other Historical, Poetical, and Prophetical books fit into this Old Testament story in various places, as shown by the vertical placement, and also provide additional information to the story.

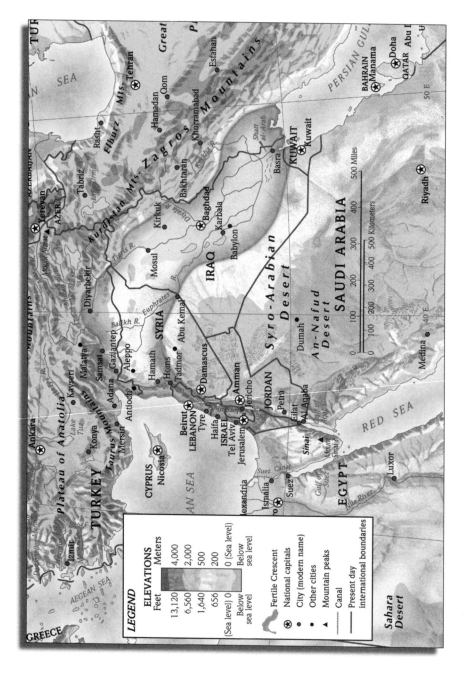

Modern States and the Ancient Near East from Holman Bible Atlas © 1998, Holman Bible Publishers. Used by permission.

THE TRIBAL ALLOTMENTS OF ISRAEL

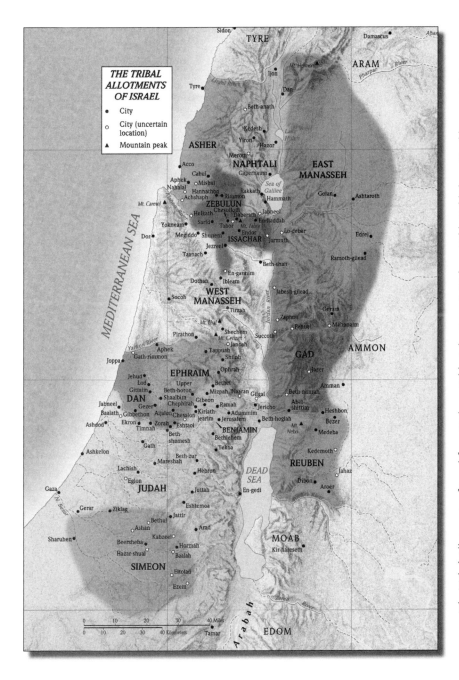

The Tribal Allotments of Israel from Holman Bible Atlas © 1998, Holman Bible Publishers. Used by permission.

THE JUDGES OF ISRAEL

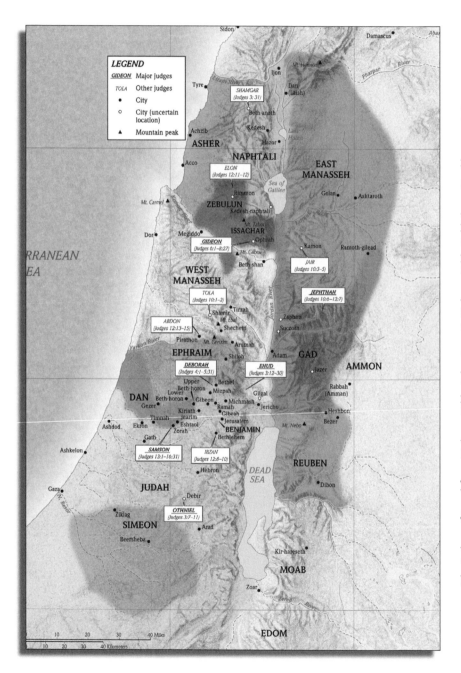

LEGEND

GIDEON	Major judges
TOLA	Other judges
•	City
○	City (uncertain location)
▲	Mountain peak

Sidon

Damascus

Abar

Ijon

Mt. Hermon

Pharpar River

Tyre

Dan (Laish)

SHAMGAR
(Judges 3: 31)

Beth-anath

Kedesh

Achzib

Hazor

ASHER

Acco

NAPHTALI

ELON
(Judges 12:11–12)

EAST MANASSEH

Golan

Ashtaroth

Mt. Carmel

Rimmon

Sea of Galilee

ZEBULUN

Kedesh-naphtali

Dor

Megiddo

Mt. Tabor

ISSACHAR

GIDEON
(Judges 6:1–8:27)

Ophrah

Mt. Gilboa

Kamon

Ramoth-gilead

Beth-shan

JAIR
(Judges 10:3–5)

WEST MANASSEH

TOLA
(Judges 10:1–2)

JEPHTHAH
(Judges 10:6–12:7)

Shamir

Tirzah

Zaphon

Mt. Ebal

Succoth

ABDON
(Judges 12:13–15)

Shechem

Pirathon

Mt. Gerizim

Arumah

GAD

EPHRAIM

Shiloh

Adam

DEBORAH
(Judges 4:1–5:31)

EHUD
(Judges 3:12–30)

AMMON

Jazer

Upper Beth-horon

Bethel

Mizpah

Rabbah (Amman)

DAN

Lower Beth-horon

Gezer

Gibeon

Gilgal

Michmash

Jericho

Ramah

Heshbon

Timnah

Kiriath-jearim

Gibeah

Bezer

Ashdod

Ekron

Eshtaol

Jerusalem

Mt. Nebo

Gath

Zorah

BENJAMIN

Ashkelon

Bethlehem

SAMSON
(Judges 13:1–16:31)

IBZAN
(Judges 12:8–10)

REUBEN

DEAD SEA

Dibon

Gaza

Hebron

Ziklag

Debir

JUDAH

OTHNIEL
(Judges 3:7–11)

Arad

SIMEON

Beersheba

Kir-hareseth

MOAB

Zoar

Zered River

10 20 30 40 Miles
10 20 30 40 Kilometers

EDOM

MEDITERRANEAN SEA

The Judges of Israel from Holman Bible Atlas © 1998, Holman Bible Publishers. Used by permission.

KINGDOM OF DAVID AND SOLOMON

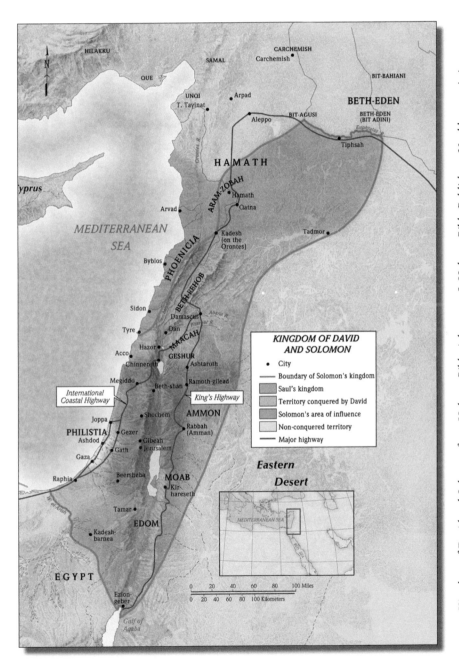

THE KINGDOMS OF ISRAEL AND JUDAH

THE KINGDOMS OF ISRAEL AND JUDAH

- • City
- ★ Capital city
- ○ City (uncertain location)
- ▲ Mountain peak
-     Israel
-     Judah
- —— International roads
- —— Local roads

MEDITERRANEAN SEA

PHOENICIA

Sidon

Ijon · Mt. Hermon · Damascus

Tyre · Abel beth-maacah · Dan

Jeroboam built a sanctuary

ARAM

Achzib · Kedesh

Hazor · Huleh

Acco

Chinnereth

Sea of Galilee · GESHUR

Gath-hepher · Aphek · Ashtaroth

Mt. Carmel

Megiddo · Dor · Mt. Tabor · Edrei

Taanach · Jezreel · Mt. Gilboa · Ramoth-gilead

Dothan · Beth-shan · Pehel

Ibleam · Jabesh-gilead

Socoh · Tirzah

Samaria · Mt. Ebal · ISRAEL · Mahanaim

Political capital of Israel from Omri onward

Shechem · Penuel · Succoth · Adam

Joppa · Aphek · Mt. Gerizim

Shiloh · Jeroboam built a sanctuary

Upper Beth-horon · Bethel · Rabbah (Amman)

Lower Beth-horon · Mizpah · Jericho · AMMON

Gezer · Geba · Heshbon

Ashdod · Aijalon · Ramah · Gibeah

Ekron · Jerusalem · Mt. Nebo · Medeba

Ashkelon · Gath · Azekah · Bethlehem

Mareshah · Beth-zur · Tekoa

Gaza · Lachish · Hebron · Ziph · Dibon

Gerar · Adoraim · Carmel · DEAD SEA · Arnon River

JUDAH · Maon

Beersheba · Arad · Kir-hareseth

Negeb · MOAB

Zered River

Eastern Desert

Tamar

Bozrah

Kadesh-barnea

EDOM

0 10 20 30 40 50 Miles
0 10 20 30 40 50 Kilometers

International Coastal Highway · King's Highway · Litani River · Yarkon River · Kishon River · Yarmuk River · Jabbok River

The Kingdoms of Israel and Judah from Holman Bible Atlas © 1998, Holman Bible Publishers. Used by permission.

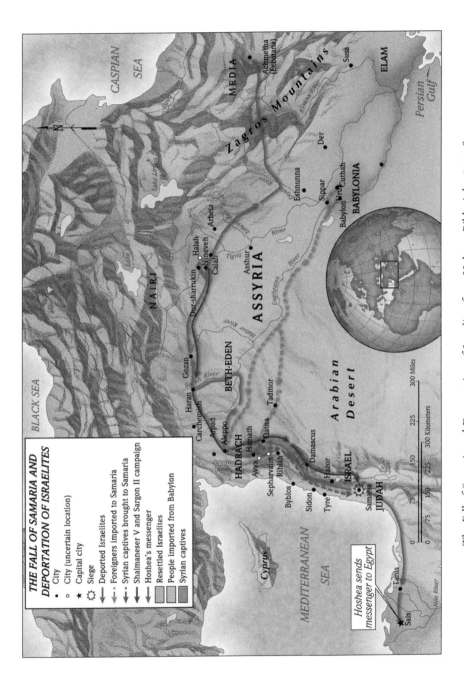

The Fall of Samaria and Deportation of Israelites from Holman Bible Atlas © 1998,
Holman Bible Publishers. Used by permission.

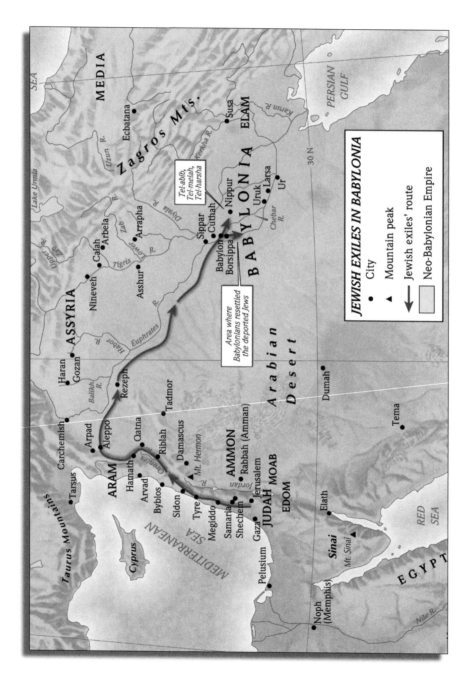

Jewish Exiles in Babylonia from Holman Bible Atlas © 1998, Holman Bible Publishers. Used by permission.

ANSWER KEY TO OUTLINES

Joshua

I. The Israelites <u>entered</u> the Promised Land (Joshua 1–5).

A. God gave a <u>charge</u> to Joshua (Joshua 1).

B. Joshua sent out two <u>spies</u> (Joshua 2).

C. God parted the <u>Jordan</u> River and the Israelites crossed over (Joshua 3–4).

D. Joshua <u>worshiped</u> the captain of the Lord's host (Joshua 5).

II. The Israelites <u>conquered</u> the Promised Land (Joshua 6–12).

A. God gave the Israelites victory at <u>Jericho</u> (Joshua 6).

B. Because of disobedience, the Israelites were disciplined at <u>Ai</u> (Joshua 7).

C. The Israelites approach to Canaan was <u>divide</u> and conquer (Joshua 9–12).

III. The Israelites <u>divided</u> the land among the twelve tribes (Joshua 13–24).

A. The <u>Gibeonites</u> were allowed to live among the Israelites.

B. The <u>Levites</u> received the sacrifice of God as their inheritance, not land (Joshua 21).

C. Joshua gave a final <u>charge</u> to the people of Israel (Joshua 22:24-28).

D. There were three burials at the end of Joshua (Joshua 24:29-33):

1. <u>Joshua</u>

2. <u>Joseph's bones</u>

3. <u>Eleazar</u>

JUDGES

I. THE CAUSES OF ISRAEL'S FAILURE (JUDGES 1–2)

A. Joshua died but his godly influence lived on through surviving ELDERS.

B. The Israelites rebelled against God and worshiped IDOLS.

C. The elders died and the new generation did not know God nor the WORK He had done for Israel.

D. God's hand was against the Israelites, and they were oppressed and DISCIPLINED by other nations.

E. The sin CYCLES followed this pattern: Israel rebelled — God rejected — Israel repented — God rescued — Israel rested.

F. There are SEVEN cycles of sin in the book of Judges.

II. THE CYCLES OF ISRAEL'S FAILURE (JUDGES 3–16)

A. Though a woman, DEBORAH led Israel to victory against Jabor, king of Canaan.

1. Women are uniquely made to be uniquely used by God.

2. Under Deborah's rule, Israel enjoyed peace for FORTY years.

B. Though a man with little courage, GIDEON led Israel to victory against the Midianites.

1. God knows who we are, and He knows what we can become.

2. God is not looking for my ability but for my availability.

3. Under Gideon's rule, Israel enjoyed peace for FORTY years.

C. Though weak in self-control, SAMSON destroyed the Philistine rulers.

1. God is always ready to forgive when we ask Him.

2. Samson led Israel for TWENTY years.

III. The <u>Consequences</u> of Israel's Failure

    A. The Israelites did what was right in their <u>own</u> eyes.

    B. Wicked behavior shows the <u>depravity</u> of man without God.

Ruth

I. The Heathen: Ruth (Ruth 1)

    A. The Historical Background of Ruth

        1. Bethlehem means "House of <u>Bread</u>"; yet at the time of Ruth, Bethlehem was experiencing a famine.

        2. Elimelech means "My God is <u>King</u>."

        3. Mahlon means "<u>weakly</u>," and Chilion means "pining."

        4. Naomi means "<u>lovely</u>" or "pleasant."

        5. Because there was a famine, Elimelech took his family to Moab, a country that was Israel's <u>enemy</u>.

    B. The Helplessness of Ruth

        1. Elimelech <u>died</u>.

        2. Mahlon and Chilion married <u>Moabite</u> women.

        3. Mahlon and Chilion <u>died</u>.

    C. Their only hope was for a <u>kinsman redeemer</u>.

        1. Kinsman means "relative or kin."

        2. Redeemer means "to buy back" or "to reclaim ownership."

        3. The requirements of a kinsman redeemer were:

            a. He must be <u>related</u>.

            b. He must be <u>able</u> to pay the price.

            c. He must be <u>willing</u> to reclaim ownership.

    D. A Flicker of <u>Hope</u> for Ruth

1. Ruth PLEDGED her heart and life to God and Naomi.

2. Ruth and Naomi returned to BETHLEHEM.

3. Naomi renamed herself "Mara" or "BITTER."

II. THE HOPE: BOAZ (RUTH 2–3)

A. Ruth began working in Boaz's field.

B. Boaz offered provision and protection for Ruth.

C. Boaz became Ruth's KINSMAN REDEEMER.

1. He was RELATED.

2. He was ABLE.

3. He was WILLING.

D. Boaz and Ruth married.

III. THE HEIR: OBED (RUTH 4)

A. Obed was Ruth's son, and his name means "servant."

B. Obed's son was JESSE.

C. Jesse was the father of DAVID, who became the king of Israel.

D. David was in the line of JESUS CHRIST, the King of kings and Lord of lords.

E. Jesus is our KINSMAN REDEEMER.

1. He is RELATED.

2. He was ABLE to pay the price for our sins.

3. He is WILLING.

I Samuel

I. THE LIFE OF SAMUEL (1 SAMUEL 1–8)

A. Hannah trusted God and He gave her a son, Samuel.

B. Eli, the unfaithful priest, raised Samuel from the time he was weaned.

C. Samuel's offices included:

1. He was Israel's last and most effective JUDGE.

2. He was Israel's first PROPHET.

3. He served as a PRIEST.

D. He was chosen by God for these offices.

E. He sought God's guidance through prayer all his life.

II. THE REIGN OF SAUL (1 SAMUEL 9–15)

A. Saul was Israel's FIRST king.

B. Saul was anointed by Samuel but chosen by MEN.

C. Saul was disqualified by God for his UNFAITHFULNESS.

D. He sought guidance from a MEDIUM and not from God.

E. Saul DIED after forty years as king of Israel.

III. THE FAITHFULNESS OF DAVID, GOD'S CHOSEN KING (1 SAMUEL 16–31)

A. David was anointed as Israel's king ELECT.

B. He was anointed by Samuel but chosen by GOD.

C. He was qualified to be king by his FAITHFULNESS.

D. David sought GOD and lived.

E. David trusted God and killed the Philistine GIANT, Goliath.

F. There was an ongoing conflict between MAN'S king, Saul, and GOD'S king, David.

G. David had a covenant relationship with Saul's son Jonathan.

I. David <u>Triumphed</u> in uniting the twelve tribes of Israel (2 Samuel 1–10).

  A. David ruled only one tribe, <u>Judah</u>, for seven years.

  B. David <u>United</u> the twelve tribes after the death of Saul's son.

   1. He established <u>Jerusalem</u> as the capital of Israel (2 Samuel 5).

   2. He established a strong <u>religious</u> order (2 Samuel 6).

   3. He expanded the <u>borders</u> of Israel (2 Samuel 8–10).

   4. God made a <u>covenant</u> with King David (2 Samuel 7).

II. David <u>Transgressed</u> against God (2 Samuel 11–12).

  A. David committed <u>adultery</u> with Bathsheba.

  B. David <u>murdered</u> Uriah.

  C. The prophet <u>Nathan</u> confronted David with his sin.

  D. David <u>confessed</u> and repented of his sin before God.

III. David suffered <u>troubles</u> from the consequences of his sin (2 Samuel 13–21).

  A. David's infant <u>son</u> died (2 Samuel 12).

  B. David's son Amnon <u>seduced</u> his half sister Tamar and then raped her (2 Samuel 13).

  C. Tamar's brother Absalom <u>murdered</u> Amnon.

  D. Absalom led a <u>revolt</u> against his father, David (2 Samuel 15–18).

  E. Absalom was <u>murdered</u> by David's army commander.

IV. DAVID TESTIFIED TO THE FAITHFULNESS OF GOD (2 SAMUEL 22–24).

A. In success, he praised God.

B. In sin, he repented before God.

C. In sorrow, he clung to God.

D. He was a man after God's own heart.

1 KINGS

I. THE KINGDOM WAS UNITED AND THRIVING (1 KINGS 1–11).

A. King David made a declaration that SOLOMON was to be king and then David died.

B. Solomon made his most UNWISE decision just prior to requesting wisdom from God.

1. He made an alliance with EGYPT.

2. He MARRIED one of Pharoah's daughters.

C. Solomon asked for WISDOM, and God gave him wisdom, knowledge, and enormous wealth.

D. The TEMPLE was built and dedicated to the glory of God.

E. Solomon's FAME reached throughout the ancient world.

F. Solomon's many foreign WIVES turned his heart away from God.

G. Solomon's heart was a DIVIDED heart.

II. THE KINGDOM WAS DIVIDED AND DESTROYED (1 KINGS 12–22).

A. REHOBOAM acted unwisely by disregarding the wisdom of his father, Solomon.

B. The once-united kingdom was divided into TWO separate nations.

1. The NORTHERN ten tribes were called Israel.

2. The capital was SAMARIA.

3. The southern two tribes were called J<small>UDAH</small>.

4. The capital was J<small>ERUSALEM</small>.

C. E<small>LIJAH</small> was a prophet who God used mightily in warning King Ahab.

2 K<small>INGS</small>

I. G<small>OD'S WARNINGS WERE GIVEN THROUGH</small> E<small>LIJAH AND</small> E<small>LISHA</small>.

A. After Elijah ascended into heaven in a chariot of fire, E<small>LISHA</small> succeeded him.

B. Elisha's ministry to Israel was very D<small>IFFERENT</small> from his mentor, Elijah.

C. Elisha's ministry lasted F<small>IFTY</small> years from King Jehoram to King Jehoash.

D. God will eventually judge and D<small>ISCIPLINE</small> His people.

II. T<small>HE KINGS OF</small> I<small>SRAEL</small> I<small>GNORED</small> G<small>OD'S WARNINGS</small>.

A. All the kings of the northern kingdom were E<small>VIL</small>.

B. The northern kingdom lasted T<small>WO HUNDRED</small> years.

C. Israel had N<small>INETEEN</small> kings.

D. God R<small>EMOVED</small> Israel from His sight.

E. In 722 BC, the Assyrians conquered Israel and S<small>CATTERED</small> the ten tribes.

III. T<small>HE KINGS OF</small> J<small>UDAH</small> I<small>GNORED</small> G<small>OD'S WARNINGS</small>.

A. Judah had T<small>WENTY</small> kings.

B. Only E<small>IGHT</small> kings did what was right.

C. God removed J<small>UDAH</small> from His presence.

D. The B<small>ABYLONIANS</small> conquered the southern tribes in 586 BC.

E. The people were taken to Babylon in E<small>XILE</small> for seventy years.

NOTES

JOSHUA

1. Gordon MacDonald, *The Life God Blesses* (Nashville: Nelson, 1994), p. 183.
2. A. Norman Jeffares and Martin Gray, *A Dictionary of Quotations* (New York: Barnes and Noble, Inc., 1995), p. 349.
3. Paul Lee Tan, *Encyclopedia of 7700 Illustrations: Signs of the Times* (Rockville, Md.: Assurance Publishers, 1979), p. 113.

JUDGES

1. Leon Wood, *The Distressing Days of the Judges* (Grand Rapids, Mich.: Zondervan, 1975), p. 4. Used by permission.
2. Wood, p. 4. Used by permission.

RUTH

1. W. Graham Scroggie, *Know Your Bible* (London: Pichering and Inglis, Ltd., 1940), p. 58.
2. Ralph Waldo Emerson, cited in Warren W. Wiersbe, *Be Committed* (Wheaton, Ill.: Scripture Press, 1993), p. 13.
3. Wiersbe, p. 17.
4. "To Illustrate," *Leadership: A Practical Journal for Church Leaders* 23, no. 1 (Winter 2002): 75.
5. Leon Wood, *The Distressing Days of the Judges* (Grand Rapids, Mich.: Zondervan, 1975), p. 4. Used by permission.

1 SAMUEL

1. Kevin Cashman, *Leadership from the Inside Out* (Provo, Utah: Executive Excellence Publishing, 1999), p. 51.
2. Parker J. Palmer, *Let Your Life Speak* (San Francisco: Jossey-Bass, 2000), p. 82.
3. Dallas Willard, *Renovation of the Heart* (Colorado Springs, Colo.: NavPress, 2002), p. 15.

2 Samuel

1. C. S. Lewis, *The World's Last Night: And Other Essays* (New York: Harcourt Brace Jovanovich, 1959), p. 23.

2. James Emery White, *Life-Defining Moments* (Colorado Springs, Colo.: WaterBrook, 2001), p. 161.

1 Kings

1. James S. Hewett, *Illustrations Unlimited* (Wheaton, Ill.: Tyndale, 1988), p. 21.

2. Joseph P. Free, *Archeology and Bible History*, 11th ed. (Wheaton, Ill.: Scripture Press, 1972), p. 170.

3. Richard J. Foster, *Prayer: Finding the Heart's True Home* (New York: HarperCollins, 1992), p. 179.

4. Free, p. 169.

5. Herbert Farmer, cited in Foster, p. 179.

6. Vivian Elisabeth Glyck, *12 Lessons on Life I Learned from My Garden* (Emmaus, Pa.: Daybreak Books, 1997), pp. 79-80. Used by permission.

2 Kings

1. Warren Bennis and Burt Nanus, *Leaders* (New York: Harper & Row, 1985), p. 37.

2. Steve Farrar, *Point Man: How a Man Can Lead a Family* (Portland, Oreg.: Multnomah, 1990), pp. 47-48.

3. Saint John Chrysostom, *On Wealth and Poverty*, trans. Catherine P. Roth (Crestwood, N. Y.: St. Vladimir's Seminary Press, 1984), p. 59.

Leader's Guide

1. *Webster's New Collegiate Dictionary* (Springfield, Mass.: G&C Merriam Co. Publishers, 1960), p. 237.

2. John K. Brilhart, *Effective Group Discussion* (Dubuque, Iowa: Wm. C. Brown Company Publishers, 1967), p. 26.

3. *How to Lead Small Group Bible Studies* (Colorado Springs, Colo.: NavPress, 1982), pp. 40-42.

BIOGRAPHIES

PAT HARLEY
Teacher

Pat committed her life to Jesus Christ at the age of thirty-two after He powerfully intervened and healed her broken marriage. After eight years of study, she began teaching the Bible to women, convinced that it is the Word of God that offers help and hope for women today. She is the founder and president of Big Dream Ministries, Inc. and served for eighteen years as the director of The Women's Fellowship, a former ministry to over five hundred women. She also served as the director of women's ministries at Fellowship Bible Church in Roswell, Georgia. Pat has a master of arts degree in education from Western Michigan University and has taken courses at Dallas Theological Seminary. She and her husband have two married daughters and several grandchildren.

ELEANOR LEWIS
Teacher

At the age of twenty-six, Eleanor accepted Christ for assurance of heaven. However, when her son was born with a severe birth defect, she turned to God's Word for answers and found not only a Savior but an all-powerful Lord. The Word of God came alive for her, and she began teaching and speaking at Christian women's clubs. For almost thirty years, she has taught Bible studies in churches, homes, and offices. In addition, she speaks at conferences and retreats across the country and internationally. She is president of Insights and Beginnings, Inc., which produced a video series and Bible study to help people understand their temperament types, overcome weaknesses, and use their strengths for the glory of God. Eleanor and her husband live in the Atlanta area and have a married son and one grandchild.

MARGIE RUETHER
Teacher

Though Margie was not raised in a churchgoing home, her parents committed their lives to Christ after Margie was in college. It was her mother's godly example and prayers that brought Margie to the throne of grace. Her growing love for Jesus and His Word led her to Bible Study Fellowship International, an interdenominational Christian organization in which laypeople teach Bible studies. After many years of study, she became a Substitute Teaching Leader and a member of the area team. She served there for a number of years before becoming one of the lead teachers at The Women's Fellowship in Roswell, Georgia. She has also facilitated a Bible teacher-training program for women and speaks at retreats and church conferences. She and her family live in Delaware.

LINDA SWEENEY
Teacher

Linda accepted Christ as her personal Savior when she was twelve years old. As an adult, she grew to love God's Word more and more. She began to see God change not only her life but the lives of others when they adhere to the wisdom of Scripture. Because of her passion to excite women to know the Word and to see their lives change as they respond in obedience, she began teaching the Bible to women in her church and community under God's leading. She has taught Sunday school for many years and was a much-loved Bible Study Fellowship International Teaching Leader for eight years. During that time, she not only taught hundreds of women weekly but also trained a large group of Bible Study Fellowship International leaders in her class. She has taught women's retreats and spoken at women's meetings and conferences throughout the South. She and her husband live in the Atlanta area and have a married daughter, a son, and two grandchildren.

ART VANDER VEEN
Senior Copywriter

Art began his relationship with Christ at age thirteen. In his late twenties after graduating from the University of New Mexico, he began preparing for full-time ministry. He earned a Th.M. degree from Dallas Theological Seminary and has ministered on the staff of Campus Crusade for Christ. He was one of the original team members of Walk Thru the Bible Ministries and served as chaplain for the Atlanta Falcons. In 1979, he was part of a team that founded Fellowship Bible Church in Roswell, Georgia, where he was a pastor for nearly twenty-five years. He now serves as pastor, teacher, and mentor at Roswell Community Church in the Atlanta area. Art is passionate about helping people understand the

Scriptures as the revealed truth from and about God. He and his wife, Jan, have three married children and seven grandchildren.

CARRIE OTT
Editor, Designer

Carrie met Christ at an early age. All her life she has had a passion for words, and as a free-lance writer and designer, this passion doubles when it is words — seen, read, and grasped — that attempt to sketch a portrait of the mystery and wonder of God and His Word. Carrie identifies with Mechtild of Magdeburg, who said, "Of the heavenly things God has shown me, I can speak but a little word, no more than a honeybee can carry away on its foot from an overflowing jar." Carrie and her husband have three children and live in the Atlanta area.

To learn more about
Big Dream Ministries, Inc. and
The Amazing Collection,
visit their website at:

www.theamazingcollection.org

LEADER'S GUIDE

Leading a group Bible study can be a challenging but incredibly rewarding experience. This Leader's Guide will provide help with the "challenging" part, as you trust God to produce the "incredibly rewarding" piece.

This guide is not designed to take you step-by-step through the individual studies. Instead, it will offer some general guidance and instruction in principles and techniques. Most of what you learn here will not be specific to *The Amazing Collection* but applicable to many kinds of group study. The one exception is the section titled Suggested Formats.

Each section of this Leader's Guide will deal with a single subject, making it easier for you to return to the guide for future help and reference.

Thank you for accepting the challenge and responsibility of leading your group! We pray God will make this a rewarding and profitable experience for you.

DISCUSSION: THE ESSENTIAL COMPONENT

The words *small-group Bible study* are almost synonymous with the term *discussion*. While there are very significant places and purposes for lecturing (one-way communication), for the most part a small group is not one of them. Therefore, discussion is an essential component of a successful small-group experience.

Discussion is the investigation of a subject or question by two or more people using verbal dialogue. Webster defines it as "consideration of a question in open debate; argument for the sake of arriving at truth or clearing up difficulties." Additionally, the word *discuss* and its synonyms mean "to discourse about so as to reach conclusions or to convince. Discuss also implies a sifting or examining, especially by presenting considerations pro and con."[1]

Small-group Bible studies will not always include debate or argument, but there *should* always be investigation, examination, and the reaching of at least tentative conclusions.

There are many benefits to discussion-style learning compared to lectures or even to interaction that is dominated by one person. Discussion:

- Keeps every member more involved in the learning process
- Allows for self-disclosure, enabling the participants to get to know each other better
- Helps crystallize the thinking of each group member by creating a venue in which topics can be investigated at deeper levels
- Creates a more informal atmosphere, which encourages a sense of relaxed learning
- Provides the potential of uncovering misconceptions and correcting misinformation
- Fosters more permanent learning and change because people tend to better remember what is said rather than what is thought
- Builds a sense of community as participants cooperate in their search for truth and understanding

While small-group Bible studies that foster healthy discussion will realize the above benefits, the depth of any group experience is greatly enhanced by an able leader. The leader plays an important role in helping each of these seven benefits become reality. For example, in order to keep every member more involved in the learning process, the leader will need to encourage those who tend to hide and manage those who tend to dominate. The other benefits require similar sensitivity by the leader. The remainder of this guide is intended to help the leader maximize these benefits for her small group.

But before we move on, one more issue should be addressed. While the leader is a crucial player in a small group, he or she should not become the person to whom all other participants address their remarks. One author has suggested that a discussion leader should strive to foster an "all-channel" network, rather than become the "hub" or center of a discussion wheel, as the following diagrams depict.

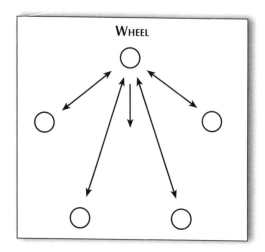

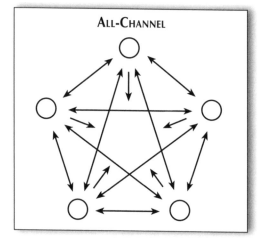

In a "wheel" network, all comments are directed toward one central leader, and he or she alone speaks to the group as a whole or to any one person.

By contrast, an "all-channel" network allows rapid communication without requiring clearance from a central gatekeeper; everyone is free to share thoughts that come to mind while they are still relevant to the topic at hand. Free exchange of questions and responses is thus encouraged.[2]

The leader's responsibility is to continually remember the need for "all-channel" communication.

LISTENING: THE LOST ART

You've probably heard it said that God gave us two ears and one mouth because He wanted us to listen twice as much as we talk. It would be difficult to prove that assumption, but the Bible *does* say:

> But everyone must be quick to hear, slow to speak. (James 1:19)

> He who gives an answer before he hears,
> It is folly and shame to him. (Proverbs 18:13)

Listening may be the most powerful tool of a successful small-group leader, but it is also possibly the most difficult trait to develop. Most people tend to talk more than listen, be more concerned about their interests than the interests of others, and listen impatiently, hoping the other person will finish quickly. True listening is a lost art, which a good small-group leader must recapture.

Listening is not just hearing. As reading is to seeing, listening is to hearing. By both reading and listening, we understand the real meaning of the words our senses "take in."

Consider the following ideas and use them to evaluate your own listening habits and skills. Then, decide which areas you could intentionally improve.

Listening Characteristics:
- It is active, not passive, and therefore sometimes tiring.

- It is other-centered, not self-centered, and therefore sometimes sacrificial.

- It is crucial, not peripheral, and therefore indispensable.

- It is difficult, not easy, and therefore often neglected.

- It is scarce, not common, and therefore greatly desirable.

Listening is not *like:*

- A chess game — planning your next verbal move while the other person is talking

- A trial — judging what is said or how it is said

- A 100-yard dash — thinking how quickly you can end the discussion

Listening is like:

- A sponge — absorbing as much as possible of what is being said and the feelings behind it

- A pair of binoculars — fixing attention on and bringing into clear focus what is being said

Kinds of Questions:

- Information — "What did you do today?"

- Opinion — "Why do you think that happened?"

- Feeling — "How do you feel about that?"

Kinds of Responses:

- Clarification — "I think what you're saying is . . ." This gets at the meaning of what was said.

- Observation — "I noticed that your voice dropped when . . ." This acknowledges the importance of nonverbal cues.

- Reflection — "You seem quite sad about . . ." This acknowledges the emotional component.

- Inquiry — "Tell me more about . . ." This seeks additional information and often gleans further insight.

While you are listening, consider silently praying for wisdom:

- "God, what are you doing in this person's heart right now?"

- "Father, help me to hear what she is really saying."

- "Eternal Counselor, what kind of response do you want me to make to what this person is saying?"

There will be times as a small-group leader when you will need to limit one member's input to allow for total group input. Your aim is not to encourage never-ending dialogue with one person, but to bring the most and the best out of each participant and the group as a whole, maximizing discussion, insight, and impact more fully than you may have thought possible.

QUESTIONS: THE MENTAL CROWBARS

Good questions can spell the difference between success and failure in a small-group setting. As you lead discussions of *The Amazing Collection*, the Learning for Life discussion questions at the beginning of each study will give you an excellent starting point. But there will be times when you will want to probe differently or more deeply. At such times, forming good questions will be incredibly important.

Some of these questions may be prepared ahead of time. Others will be developed as you go. Remember, every good question shares some common characteristics:

- Brief — short and uncluttered
- Applicable — relevant to the people's needs
- Simple — easily understood
- Interesting — capable of holding attention
- Conforming — based on the material being studied

As a leader you may ask launching, guiding, and application questions. The following material describes these three types of questions, giving examples of each.

Launching Questions:
- Initiate meaningful discussion on a subject
- May be prepared ahead of time
- Will determine to a large extent the direction your discussion will take
- Are general questions intended to stimulate discussion
- Must be based on the participants' previous study to enable quality contributions

  Examples:
  - "What did you discover in this passage about . . . ?"
  - "What impressed you most about how God . . . ?"
  - "What thoughts do you have about Moses after this study?"
  - "Why do you think God included this passage in the Bible?"
  - "How would you describe the holiness of God?"

Guiding Questions:
- Keep the discussion moving, drawing out the most important ideas and refocusing a wandering discussion
- May be prepared ahead of time as you anticipate the subjects that will be raised by the group

- May be crafted as the discussion is in high gear (This takes practice!)
- Take the participants beyond initial observations and more deeply into the meaning of the material

   Examples:
   - "Sally just mentioned the concept of obedience. How does that fit with what this passage seems to say?"
   - "Who else would like to comment on that?"
   - "We've said a lot of things about grace in our discussion. If you had to boil it down to a sentence, what would you say?"
   - "What we're discussing is interesting, but we've wandered from where we want to go. Can someone take us back to where we veered off the trail?"

Application Questions:
- Are supplied for you in *The Amazing Collection* workbooks
- May be developed based on your own knowledge of the group
- May be difficult to formulate but serve as the bridge from Bible study to daily living—from the head to the heart
- Do not always involve something concrete to do or to change
- Could include meditation, reflection, remembering, or simply waiting on God
- May be questions that will encourage the group to share their answers aloud or may suggest a more private response
- May be specific or general
- Must relate to the truth the group has just studied

   Examples:
   - "Write a prayer pouring out your heart to God in response to what He has been teaching you this week."
   - "Do you know someone who models well what we have just studied? How could you affirm that person this week?"
   - "What do you sense God is asking you to do in response to your study?"
   - "What do you see in this character's life that you would like to imitate? What would that look like? What is the first step?"

Crafting and asking questions are skills that can be developed and honed. After each group meeting, it might be useful to evaluate your questions. Did they lead the group where you sensed God wanted to lead? Which "as you go" guiding questions worked well or not so well? How did the group respond to the questions? Was there any confusion? Finally, make a point to review anything you learned about asking questions each week.

ROLES PEOPLE PLAY: THE ULTIMATE CHALLENGE

If being a small-group Bible study leader involved only facilitating discussion, learning to listen well, and forging meaningful questions, the challenge would be large enough. But add to that the fact that every person in your group will have different needs, temperaments and personalities, approaches to Bible study, reasons for being there, and levels of maturity, and the role of leadership becomes exponentially more challenging.

Professor Howard Hendricks of Dallas Theological Seminary describes in *How to Lead Small Group Bible Studies* some of the roles people play in group situations. You may find these helpful in evaluating your own group's dynamic.

Immature roles

The onlooker	Content to be a silent spectator. Only nods, smiles, and frowns. Other than this, he is a passenger instead of a crew member.
The monopolizer	Brother Chatty. Rambles roughshod over the rest of the conversation with his verbal dexterity. Tenaciously clings to his right to say what he thinks — even without thinking.
The belittler	This is Mr. Gloom. He minimizes the contributions of others. Usually has three good reasons why some opinion is wrong.
The wisecrack	Feels called to a ministry of humor. Mr. Cheerio spends his time as the group playboy. Indifferent to the subject at hand, he is always ready with a clever remark.
The hitchhiker	Never had an original thought in his life. Unwilling to commit himself. Sits on the sidelines until others reach a conclusion, then jumps on the bandwagon.
The pleader	Chronically afflicted with obsessions. Always pleading for some cause or action. Feels led to share this burden frequently. One-track mind.
The sulker	Lives with a resentful mood. The group won't always agree entirely with his views, so he sulks.

Mature roles

The proposer	Initiates ideas and action. Keeps things moving.
The encourager	Brings others into the discussion. Encourages others to contribute. Emphasizes the value of their suggestions and comments. Stimulates others to greater activity by approval and recognition.

The clarifier	Has the ability to step in when confusion, chaos, and conflict occur. He defines the problem concisely. Points out the issues clearly.
The analyzer	Examines the issues closely. Weighs suggestions carefully. Never accepts anything without first thinking it through.
The explorer	Always moving into new and different areas. Probes relentlessly. Never satisfied with the obvious or the traditional viewpoints.
The mediator	Promotes harmony between members—especially those who have trouble agreeing. Seeks to find conclusions acceptable to all.
The synthesizer	Able to put the pieces together from different ideas and viewpoints.[3]

No doubt you will see some of these roles typified by members of your small group. How you deal with members who play out the immature roles and how you encourage and utilize those who take on the mature ones will be an ongoing challenge. Ask the Spirit of God to give you sensitivity, creativity, and ability as you lead. Pray for wisdom to become your constant, ready resource.

YOUR LEADERSHIP: A SPIRITUAL ENDEAVOR

Before we move on, it is important to remember that beyond understanding and fostering discussion, learning to listen well, developing your skill in fashioning questions, and learning to lead different kinds of people, it is God who supplies the grace and strength that will carry you through the challenges of leadership.

This Leader's Guide has focused so far on you and your best efforts, but in truth you will accomplish absolutely nothing of eternal value unless the Spirit of God takes your faithful efforts and infuses them with His enabling power and grace.

For this reason, we encourage you to prepare and lead in complete humility, dependence, and trust, remembering these critical precepts:

I can do all things through Him who strengthens me. (Philippians 4:13)

"My grace is sufficient for you, for power is perfected in weakness." (2 Corinthians 12:9)

"I am the vine, you are the branches; he who abides in Me and I in him, he bears much fruit, for apart from Me you can do nothing." (John 15:5)

Finally, be strong in the Lord and in the strength of His might. Put on the full armor of God, that you will be able to stand firm against the schemes of the devil. (Ephesians 6:10-11)

Our prayer for you is that of Paul's prayers for the Ephesians:

That the God of our Lord Jesus Christ, the Father of glory, may give to you a spirit of wisdom and of revelation in the knowledge of Him. I pray that the eyes of your heart may be enlightened, so that you will know what is the hope of His calling, what are the riches of the glory of His inheritance in the saints, and what is the surpassing greatness of His power toward us who believe. These are in accordance with the working of the strength of His might. . . . [And] that He would grant you, according to the riches of His glory, to be strengthened with power through His Spirit in the inner man, so that Christ may dwell in your hearts through faith; and that you, being rooted and grounded in love, may be able to comprehend with all the saints what is the breadth and length and height and depth, and to know the love of Christ which surpasses knowledge, that you may be filled up to all the fullness of God. Now to Him who is able to do far more abundantly beyond all that we ask or think, according to the power that works within us, to Him be the glory in the church and in Christ Jesus to all generations forever and ever. Amen. (Ephesians 1:17-19; 3:16-21)

APPENDIX A

THE EFFECTIVE DISCUSSION LEADER: A WORTHY GOAL

This section presents a model for the effective discussion leader (EDL). You may not demonstrate every characteristic listed, nor do you need to. Some of these things you will do very well; others you will do okay; still others may be a weak area for you. That is just fine. Consider this list simply an ideal to aim for. Our hope is that it will motivate you to grow as a small-group leader by revealing your areas of strength and highlighting your areas of weakness for which you may need help. God never said He could use only perfect people in ministry. In fact, your limitations in one or more of these areas may allow for others in the group to come alongside and complement you by contributing their strengths.

You may choose to use this list with a group of leaders to discuss your common ministries and responsibilities and share with each other challenges and successes you've experienced as leaders. Hearing others' thoughts about each of these characteristics might encourage you as you continue to grow.

What key characteristics make an effective discussion leader?

1. EDLs have a good grasp of the material to be discussed.

   - They have studied the material in advance.
   - They have a clear purpose for the meeting.
   - They have an introduction planned.
   - They have questions planned.
   - They have a tentative conclusion in mind.
   - They have examined their own life in relation to the truth of the study.
   - They seek to be diligent workers who accurately handle the word of truth (see 2 Timothy 2:15).

2. EDLs are skilled in organizing group thinking.

   - They know how to use questions.

- They can detect tangents and gently but firmly bring the discussion back on track.

3. EDLs are open-minded.
   - They express judgments in a conditional way.
   - They encourage consideration of all points of view.
   - They encourage open-mindedness on the part of all the members.
   - They are able to handle incorrect answers by inviting further questioning or discussion.

4. EDLs are active participants.
   - They talk frequently yet not excessively.
   - They are not defensive or sensitive to disagreement or criticism.

5. EDLs are facilitators.
   - They do not give dictatorial directions.
   - They encourage participation by all.
   - They encourage interaction among all members.
   - They are able to manage members who tend to dominate discussion.
   - They are able to stimulate and involve shy or reticent members in nonthreatening ways.

6. EDLs speak well.
   - They speak clearly.
   - They speak in a concise, pertinent way.
   - They are not tactless, chattering, offensive speakers.

7. EDLs have respect for and sensitivity to others.
   - They are empathetic.
   - They do not attack others.
   - They do not cause others to "lose face."
   - They are aware of how others are reacting.
   - They are patient.

8. EDLs are self-controlled.
   - They can remain impartial when necessary.

- They can express their feelings in a direct, yet nonaccusatory manner.

9. EDLs can assume different roles.
   - They can give encouragement.
   - They can give direction when necessary.
   - They can insert humor to break the tension when appropriate.
   - They can lead the group in prayer to seek wisdom.
   - They can give personal attention to needy members.

10. EDLs give credit to the group and its members.
    - They praise the group for insights and progress.
    - They stress teamwork.
    - They make all the members feel important.
    - They value others as their equals.
    - They "do nothing from selfishness or empty conceit" but regard others as more important than themselves (Philippians 2:3).

11. EDLs are authentically transparent.
    - They share personal illustrations.
    - They share personal weaknesses, frustrations, pressures, and failures without seeking undue personal attention.
    - They share personal feelings.
    - They share personal requests.
    - They plan ahead so all this can be done with taste and genuineness.

12. EDLs are enthusiastic.
    - They pour themselves into the subject and the discussion of it.
    - They allow the subject to be poured into them by God prior to the discussion.
    - They recognize that genuine enthusiasm is a powerful motivator for others.

13. EDLs are properly critical and evaluative of their leadership.
    - They constantly look for ways to improve.
    - They regularly seek feedback and advice.
    - They consistently evaluate the various aspects of their leadership role.

- They remember that evaluation is not comparing themselves with others but is seeking the Holy Spirit's input on possible improvement.

14. EDLs know that leadership is a spiritual endeavor.

   - They regularly admit to God that apart from Him they can do nothing (see John 15:5).

   - They confidently say "I can do all things" and then humbly add "through Him who strengthens me" (Philippians 4:13).

   - They never forget God's promise that "My grace is sufficient for you" (2 Corinthians 12:9).

APPENDIX B

SUGGESTED FORMATS FOR *THE AMAZING COLLECTION*

The Amazing Collection is intentionally flexible to accommodate a variety of teaching settings and calendars. It is possible to complete the study of all sixty-six books of the Bible in two years by teaching a book a week for thirty-three weeks each year (excluding summers and holidays).

Another option would be to go through the material in three years, teaching a book a week for twenty-two weeks each year, perhaps beginning in September and going through April. Also, for individuals, the program could be completed in approximately fifteen months, studying a book a week for sixty-six consecutive weeks.

There is flexibility in each individual session as well. Sessions might last an hour, in which the group watches the video (forty-five minutes) and allows fifteen minutes for discussion. Or, a 1.5-hour format could include the video, fifteen minutes for refreshments, fifteen for discussion, and fifteen for homework review. If time permits, two-hour sessions could include the video, refreshments, thirty minutes for discussion, and thirty for homework review.

Maybe you'll discover another format that suits your group to a tee. Feel free to use it!

APPENDIX C

SHARING THE GOSPEL

Leaders should be sensitive to the fact that some group members may have an interest in the Bible without having established a personal relationship with its central figure, Jesus Christ.

Sharing the gospel is quite easy for some people and more challenging for others. But if you sense that there are members in your group who would benefit from a clear explanation of salvation, by all means, offer one! There may even be "natural" openings during your course of study (at the end of a book or workbook or during your study of the Gospels or the book of Romans) when the gospel seems to "tell itself." In addition, the vast majority of discussion questions (Old and New Testament) contain a question that points directly to the person of Jesus Christ. These are "teachable moments." Don't miss them.

Several excellent tools exist that can help you walk an unbeliever through the basics of salvation. *The Four Spiritual Laws, Steps to Peace with God, My Heart — Christ's Home,* and *The Roman Road* are just a few. The leaders in your church may be able to provide you with one or more of them.

Although there are many excellent video testimonies throughout *The Amazing Collection,* it may be appropriate at some point to briefly share your own personal testimony with your group or with one or more of its members. It may help to think of your "story" in four parts: your life before Christ, how you came to know and understand your need for forgiveness and reconciliation with God, what Christ did on your behalf on the cross, and how your life is different today having accepted His atoning sacrifice on your behalf. This is your story! Pray for a sensitive heart, the right timing, and the right words to share it when the Holy Spirit leads you to do so.

It is our prayer that no one would complete *The Amazing Collection* without a personal, saving knowledge of our Savior, the Lord Jesus Christ.